LAB MANUAL AND WORKBOOK

The Pharmacy Technician: Foundations and Practices

MIKE JOHNSTON, CPHT

CLIFFORD FRANK, CPHT

MICHELLE GOEKING, BM, CPHT

MICHAEL HAYTER, PHARMD, MBA

ROBIN LUKE, CPHT

SECOND CUSTOM EDITION

Taken from:
Lab Manual and Workbook to accompany *The Pharmacy Technician: Foundations and Practices by Mike Johnston, Karen Davis, and Jeff Gricar*
by Mike Johnston, Clifford Frank, Michelle Goeking,
Michael M. Hayter, and Robin Luke

Learning Solutions

New York Boston San Francisco
London Toronto Sydney Tokyo Singapore Madrid
Mexico City Munich Paris Cape Town Hong Kong Montreal

Taken from:

Lab Manual and Workbook to accompany *The Pharmacy Technician: Foundations and Practices by Mike Johnston, Karen Davis, and Jeff Gricar*
by Mike Johnston, Clifford Frank, Michelle Goeking, Michael M. Hayter, and Robin Luke

Upper Saddle River, New Jersey 07458

This special edition published in cooperation with Pearson Learning Solutions.

Pearson Learning Solutions, 501 Boylston Street, Suite 900, Boston, MA 02116
A Pearson Education Company
www.pearsoned.com

Printed in the United States of America

5 6 7 8 9 10 V001 16 15 14 13 12

000200010270737284

RG

ISBN 10: 0-558-78635-9
ISBN 13: 978-0-558-78635-9

Contents

Preface

The Pharmacy Technician: Foundations and Practices addresses today's comprehensive educational needs for one of the fastest-growing jobs in the United States: that of the pharmacy technician. The pharmacy technician career is ranked 60th among the 100 fastest-growing jobs in the United States and 19th among the 500 best jobs for people with a conventional personality type. According to the U.S. Bureau of Labor Statistics, the pharmacy technician career is growing at approximately 30 percent annually, a much higher rate than other jobs in the health professions. This equates to more than 39,000 pharmacy technician job openings available every year.

In addition to the tremendous workforce demand for pharmacy technicians, professional regulations and requirements are being established for pharmacy technicians across the United States. With many State Boards of Pharmacy either considering, or having already enacted, mandatory registration, certification, and/or formal education, the need for a comprehensive and up-to-date pharmacy technician textbook like *The Pharmacy Technician: Foundations and Practices* has never been greater.

This *Workbook/Lab Manual to Accompany The Pharmacy Technician: Foundations and Practices* is designed to give you additional practice in mastering the varied skills that will be required of you as a pharmacy technician. It is organized to correspond with the 34 chapters in the textbook. Each workbook/lab manual chapter includes:

- Learning objectives from the textbook, with references to related activities within the workbook/lab manual.
- An introduction that summarizes the main themes from the textbook chapter.
- Review Questions that evaluate your comprehension of the textbook chapter content. Question types include multiple choice, fill-in-the-blank, matching, and true/false.
- Pharmacy Calculation Problems that will give you additional practice and help increase your comfort level in using the math skills you will need on a daily basis as a practicing pharmacy technician.
- PTCB Exam Practice Questions related to the chapter's specific content that will help you prepare for the Pharmacy Technician Certification Exam.
- Activities in certain chapters challenge you to explore facets of the chapter material more thoroughly and offer a variety of exercises, including anatomy worksheets, case studies with critical thinking questions, Web research problems, and role-playing scenarios.
- Hands-on Lab activities in certain chapters give you the chance to practice procedures, work with equipment, or perform additional research.

Be sure to visit the Companion website for this text. It includes an online study guide that contains helpful links, self-test questions, and an online glossary. You will be able to submit your results for a score that you can send to your professor or to yourself for further evaluation. This resource, combined with the Student CD packaged with the textbook, will give you the opportunity to put into practice those skills you are being taught in the classroom.

About NPTA

The National Pharmacy Technician Association (NPTA) is the world's largest professional organization specifically for pharmacy technicians. The association is dedicated to advancing the value of pharmacy technicians and the vital roles they play in pharmaceutical care. In a society of countless associations, we believe it takes much more than just a mission statement to meet the professional needs of and provide the necessary leadership for the pharmacy technician profession—it takes action and results.

The organization is composed of pharmacy technicians practicing in a variety of practice settings, such as retail, independent, hospital, mail-order, home care, long-term care, nuclear, military, correctional facilities, formal education, training, management, sales, and many more. NPTA is a reflection of this diverse profession and provides unparallel support and resources to members.

NPTA is the foundation of the pharmacy technician profession; we have an unprecedented past, a strong presence, and a promising future. We are dedicated to improving our profession while remaining focused on our members.

Pharmacy technician students are welcome to join more than 30,000 practicing pharmacy technicians as members of NPTA.

For more information:
call 888-247-8706
visit www.pharmacytechnician.org

CHAPTER 1

History of Pharmacy Practice

After completing Chapter 1 from the textbook, you should be able to:	Related Activity in the Workbook/Lab Manual
1. Describe the origins of the practice of pharmacy from the Age of Antiquity.	Review Questions, PTCB Exam Practice Questions
2. Discuss changes in the practice of pharmacy during the Middle Ages.	Review Questions, PTCB Exam Practice Questions
3. Describe changes in the practice of pharmacy during the Renaissance.	Review Questions, PTCB Exam Practice Questions
4. List significant milestones for the practice of pharmacy from the 18th, 19th, and 20th centuries.	Review Questions, PTCB Exam Practice Questions
5. Discuss the role biotechnology and genetic engineering could have on the future of pharmacy practice.	Review Questions

INTRODUCTION

The practice of pharmacy has ancient roots. The word *pharmacy* comes from the Greek word *pharmakon*, meaning "drug," and the origin of pharmacy practice goes back to ancient times, more than 7,000 years ago. The role of a pharmacy technician can be traced back to 2900 BCE, in ancient Egypt, where echelons were gatherers and preparers of drugs, similar to the modern-day pharmacy technician; chiefs of fabrication were the head pharmacists.

The history of pharmacy practice may seem to be unnecessary to you as you prepare to become a pharmacy technician. However, if you are to understand many of the concepts, theories, and practices covered in this workbook/laboratory manual and the textbook, you need to understand the evolution of the pharmacy profession. Many of the principles used in pharmacy thousands of years ago are still practiced today. Understanding the historic roots will also help you appreciate the areas in which the profession has evolved and how professional guidelines and regulations have developed. As you will discover, the responsibilities of and opportunities for pharmacy technicians continue to evolve, along with the profession of pharmacy itself.

REVIEW QUESTIONS

Match the following.

1. _____ pharmacogenomics
2. _____ pharmacy
3. _____ prescription
4. _____ apothecary
5. _____ biotechnology
6. _____ pharmacopoeia
7. _____ compounding

a. Latin term for pharmacist
b. Producing, mixing, or preparing a drug by combining ingredients
c. Use of living things to make or modify a product
d. An order to prepare/dispense
e. Study of genetic differences in responses to drug therapy
f. Art/science of preparing and dispensing medication
g. Book of products, formulae, and directions for preparation

Choose the best answer.

8. The word *pharmacy* comes from which ancient Greek word for drug?
   a. pharmakos
   b. pharmakopeia
   c. pharmakon
   d. pharmakot

9. Which of the following is supposedly an abbreviation for the Latin word for *recipe*?
   a. Rx
   b. sx
   c. tx
   d. dx

10. The Age of Antiquity refers to which time period?
    a. 8000 BCE up through CE 699
    b. 5000 BCE up through CE 499
    c. 3000 BCE up through CE 899
    d. 4000 BCE up through CE 599

11. The "father of botany" is considered to be:
    a. Shen Nung.
    b. Echelon.
    c. Theophrastus.
    d. Charaka Samhita.

Match the following scientists with their accomplishments.

12. _____ Galen
13. _____ Mithridates
14. _____ Hippocrates
15. _____ Pedanios Dioscorides

a. developed the theory of humors
b. poisons and poison preventatives
c. rules for drug collection, storage, and use
d. established principles of compounding

Choose the best answer.

16. The first apothecaries, or privately owned drugstores, were established in the late eighth century by the:
    a. Arabs.
    b. Greeks.
    c. Romans.
    d. Italians.

17. The first pharmacy technicians in ancient Egypt were known as:
    a. slaves.
    b. ebers.
    c. echelons.
    d. chiefs of fabrication.

18. America's first female pharmacist was the granddaughter of:
    a. an indentured servant named Dremmell Marshall and was named Isabell.
    b. a pharmacist named Christopher Marshall and was named Elizabeth.
    c. the inventor Benjamin Franklin and was named Mary.
    d. a prominent Bostonian, Andrew Craigie, and was named Alice.

19. The first school of pharmacy was:
    a. the Philadelphia College of Pharmacy.
    b. the University of Pennsylvania Pharmacy College.
    c. Boston University.
    d. the Massachusetts School of Pharmacology.

20. The American Pharmaceutical Association was opened to "all pharmacists and druggists of good character" in:
    a. 1821.
    b. 1852.
    c. 1872.
    d. 1962.

21. The *United States Pharmacopoeia* (USP) was first published in:
    a. 1820.
    b. 1877.
    c. 1822.
    d. 1869.

22. Gregor Mendel is known as the Father of Modern Genetics. He was an Austrian:
    a. pharmacist and scientist.
    b. priest and pharmacist.
    c. scientist and priest.
    d. priest and author.

23. The practice of pharmacy began to be regulated by the federal government:
    a. in the early 1900s.
    b. in the late 1800s.
    c. in the late 1900s.
    d. pharmacy has always been heavily regulated by the federal government.

24. Pharmacogenomics is the use of:
    a. genomic or genetic information to predict a drug's efficacy.
    b. personal DNA information to track patients.
    c. gene splicing to produce effective medications.
    d. a study of future drugs and their possible uses.

Match the following.

25. _____ Clinical Era	a. formulating and dispensing drugs
26. _____ Pharmaceutical Care Era	b. developing and testing drugs
27. _____ Traditional Era	c. dispensing information, warnings, and advice
28. _____ Scientific Era	d. positive outcomes of therapies

PHARMACY CALCULATION PROBLEMS

Calculate the following.

1. 62.1 + 4.5 + 2.92 + 0.6 =
2. 120 mL + 60 mL + 80 mL + 40 mL =
3. 750 mg − 80 mg − 35.5 mg =
4. 10.5 oz. + 11.5 oz. − 3.25 oz. =
5. 9.8 mL − 5.4 mL + 12.9 mL =

PTCB EXAM PRACTICE QUESTIONS

1. Which ancient civilization provides the earliest record of apothecary practice?
   a. Babylonian
   b. Chinese
   c. Indian
   d. Aztec
2. What is the name of the first woman pharmacist in America?
   a. Wilson
   b. Marshall
   c. Washington
   d. Tyler
3. In what city was the first American school of pharmacy founded?
   a. Boston
   b. Baltimore
   c. Providence
   d. Philadelphia
4. What was the first professional pharmacy association?
   a. APHA
   b. NABP
   c. ASHP
   d. ACPE
5. Hippocrates, often referred to as the "Father of Medicine," was part of which ancient culture?
   a. Egyptian
   b. Greek
   c. Roman
   d. Chinese

CHAPTER 2
The Professional Pharmacy Technician

After completing Chapter 2 from the textbook, you should be able to:	Related Activity in the Workbook/Lab Manual
1. Summarize the educational requirements and competencies of both pharmacists and pharmacy technicians.	Review Questions, PTCB Exam Practice Questions
2. Describe the two primary pharmacy practice settings and define the basic roles of pharmacists and pharmacy technicians working in each setting.	Review Questions
3. Explain six specific characteristics of a good pharmacy technician.	Review Questions
4. Demonstrate the behavior of a professional pharmacy technician.	Review Questions
5. Explain the registration/licensure and certification process for becoming a pharmacy technician.	Review Questions, PTCB Exam Practice Questions

INTRODUCTION

Pharmacy is an industry consisting of professionals: pharmacists and pharmacy technicians. Many claim—with good reason—that pharmacy is the most trusted profession in America. As with any profession, employment in this field requires you to be educated, trained, diligent, and ethical. You must maintain specific competencies, undergo specialized education and training, and exhibit key personal characteristics. The process of preparing for your future includes formal education and training, registration/licensure, national certification, and involvement with a professional organization. The benefits of your hard work and dedication are the tremendous career opportunities awaiting you as a future pharmacy technician.

REVIEW QUESTIONS

Match the following.

1. _____ certification
2. _____ licensing
3. _____ registration
4. _____ attitude
5. _____ compassion
6. _____ empathy
7. _____ ambulatory pharmacy
8. _____ community pharmacy
9. _____ health system pharmacy
10. _____ institutional pharmacy

a. process of listing/being named to a list
b. government permission to do something
c. located on site where patients reside
d. common name for health system pharmacy
e. feelings of concern and understanding
f. deep awareness and sympathy
g. retail pharmacy
h. nongovernmental verification of competency
i. chain, drug/grocery store, mail-order, home health care pharmacies
j. way of acting, thinking, or believing

True or False?

11. Historically, there were only three recognized professions: law, medicine, and ministry.
    T F
12. Pharmacy technicians must be licensed in all states.
    T F
13. A pharmacist may advise other healthcare professionals.
    T F
14. Most institutional pharmacies are open 24 hours.
    T F
15. Your body language can hide your true feelings and attitudes.
    T F

Choose the best answer.

16. Which of the following tasks is most likely to be performed by a pharmacist?
    a. insurance billing
    b. patient private information maintenance
    c. patient counseling
    d. inventory ordering
17. The set of qualities and characteristics that represent perceptions of your competence and character, as judged by your constituents, is called your:
    a. attitude.
    b. professional image.
    c. professionalism.
    d. demeanor.
18. Which of the following attire would be unacceptable for a pharmacy technician?
    a. tie
    b. lab coat
    c. shorts
    d. scrubs

19. Which is an example of adapting to change?
   a. changing priorities, strategies, or methods
   b. maintaining effectiveness
   c. handling stress properly
   d. all of the above

20. Which of the following is not a common eligibility requirement for technicians?
   a. no felony conviction(s)
   b. high school graduate or GED equivalent
   c. a two-year college degree
   d. certification

21. Pharmacy technicians are in the business of:
   a. selling drugs.
   b. patient care.
   c. patient consultations.
   d. making money.

Name four sources of CE for pharmacy technicians.

22. ______________________________
23. ______________________________
24. ______________________________
25. ______________________________

PHARMACY CALCULATION PROBLEMS

Calculate the following.

1. Bobby has completed 12 hours of CE. How many more hours does he need to complete to meet the PTCB requirements?

2. If Judy worked 38.5 hours one week and 39 hours the next week, how much would her gross pay be for those two weeks if she were paid $12.75 per hour?

3. A customer has three prescriptions and owes a co-payment of $15.00 on each one. How much will the customer be charged for all three prescriptions?

4. A technician works the third shift at a hospital for seven days in a row, followed by seven days off. She is scheduled to work Sunday through Saturday from 10:00 p.m. till 8:00 a.m., every other week. If the pay period starts on Sunday, how many hours will she work in two consecutive weeks?

10 hrs. Sunday

5. A medication order calls for a special mouthwash that the pharmacy must make. It contains 50% diphenhydramine syrup and 50% viscous lidocaine. The physician ordered 16 ounces. How much of each ingredient will you need to make this?

PTCB EXAM PRACTICE QUESTIONS

1. When a pharmacy student graduates from an accredited college of pharmacy in the United States, what degree does she or he receive?
   a. Bachelor of Science (BS)
   b. Bachelor of Arts (BA)
   c. Doctor of Pharmacy (PharmD)
   d. Master of Science (MS)

2. In the United States, pharmacy technicians are often required to be registered or licensed before they may perform the duties of a pharmacy technician. This requirement is mandated by which government agency?
   a. Food and Drug Administration (FDA)
   b. State Board of Pharmacy (SBOP)
   c. Drug Enforcement Agency (DEA)
   d. *United States Pharmacopoeia* (USP)

3. When a pharmacy technician successfully completes a certification examination to become a CPhT, this signifies to others that he or she is:
   a. smart.
   b. polite.
   c. empathetic.
   d. competent.

CHAPTER 3
Communication and Customer Care

After completing Chapter 3 from the textbook, you should be able to:	Related Activity in the Workbook/Lab Manual
1. Describe and illustrate the communication process.	Review Questions, PTCB Exam Practice Questions
2. List and explain the three types of communication.	Review Questions, PTCB Exam Practice Questions
3. Summarize the various barriers to effective communication.	Review Questions, PTCB Exam Practice Questions
4. List and describe the primary defense mechanisms.	Review Questions
5. Describe specific strategies for eliminating barriers to communication.	Review Questions, PTCB Exam Practice Questions
6. Summarize the elements of and considerations in caring for patients.	Review Questions, PTCB Exam Practice Questions
7. List the Five Rights of medication administration.	Review Questions

INTRODUCTION

Communication is simply the process of transferring information, although it is not a simple process. You communicate to get your message across to others clearly and unambiguously. Communicating takes effort from everyone involved, including the sender (the person who initiates the communication) and the receiver (the person or group the sender is addressing). The communication process often breaks down, and errors may result in misunderstandings and confusion.

As a pharmacy technician, you will need to communicate effectively with a variety of people, including your immediate co-workers, customers or patients, healthcare personnel, suppliers, drug representatives, health insurance representatives, and many others. Pharmacy technicians work as frontline employees in the pharmacy, which means that both your management and your patients will rely on you to be an effective communicator and to identify and eliminate communication barriers as they arise. Remember that becoming an effective communicator is a lifelong process that gets easier with experience and time.

REVIEW QUESTIONS

Match the following.

1._____ channel
2. _____ projection
3. _____ defense mechanisms
4. _____ denial
5. _____ feedback

a. unconscious mental process used to protect the ego
b. defense mechanism of refusing to acknowledge painful realities
c. gesture, action, sound, written or spoken word used in transmitting information
d. defense mechanism in which one's own attitudes are attributed to others
e. the return of information back to the sender

Choose the best answer.

6. Directly related to the effectiveness of communication are:
   a. customer service and pharmaceutical care.
   b. speed of medication delivery and customer care.
   c. patient satisfaction and sales.
   d. pharmacy profitability and customer service.

7. The situation or environment in which a message is delivered is called:
   a. channel.
   b. feedback.
   c. context.
   d. verbal.

8. In communicating with patients, it is best to use a:
   a. monotone, impersonal tone.
   b. condescending patient tone.
   c. sympathetic caring tone.
   d. tone that mimics the patient's.

9. Effective communication will involve all of the following except:
   a. pleasantness.
   b. active listening.
   c. professional tones.
   d. aggressiveness

10. When leaving a voicemail for a patient, it is important not to:
    a. provide personal patient information.
    b. provide your name.
    c. provide your pharmacy's phone number.
    d. repeat information you have already given.

11. Facial expressions, eye contact, posture, and silence, are forms of:
    a. communication barriers.
    b. nonverbal communication.
    c. intimidation.
    d. not as effective as the spoken word.

12. Which of the following is not a barrier to communication?
    a. inaccurate information
    b. language
    c. overly lengthy message
    d. translators

13. If a patient does not speak good English, a technician should:
    a. see if a translator is available.
    b. speak the patient's native language if possible.
    c. provide instructions in the patient's native language.
    d. all of the above.

14. Defense mechanisms share two common properties:
    a. repression and sublimation.
    b. denial and displacement.
    c. unconscious trigger and distortion of reality.
    d. projection and rationalization.

15. When an individual transfers his or her own negative emotions to someone who is unrelated to those feelings, it is called:
    a. rationalization.
    b. displacement.
    c. denial.
    d. projection.

16. A patient who is prejudiced against minorities, and complains that an Asian-American technician showed him disrespect, may be using:
    a. regression.
    b. sublimation.
    c. projection.
    d. displacement.

17. The best strategy a technician can use for pharmacy conflict resolution is to:
    a. hold one's ground.
    b. demand respect.
    c. identify who has a problem.
    d. involve the supervisor.

18. The Five Rights include all of the following except:
    a. right strength.
    b. right time.
    c. right patient.
    d. right price.

19. The Patient's Bill of Rights includes being treated with courtesy and respect. It was passed by Congress in:
    a. 1905.
    b. 2005.
    c. 1995.
    d. 1955.

20. In various states, technicians may, with the approval of a pharmacist, do all the following except:
    a. read the instructions for a prescription to a patient.
    b. assist the patient with OTC selection.
    c. provide verbal advice and/or clinical information.
    d. assist the patient with medical devices.

PHARMACY CALCULATION PROBLEMS

Calculate the following.

1. At retail price, two prescriptions would cost $48.00 and $125.00, respectively. The customer has insurance and only pays $15 per prescription. How much money did the customer save with her insurance?

2. It costs the pharmacy $28.48 for 32 ounces of guaifenesin syrup. How much does it cost per ounce?

3. If a customer pays 30% of the retail price for a medication, how much would the customer pay for a prescription with a retail price of $100?

4. A technician gets paid $12 per hour for the first 40 hours worked in a week. He gets traditional overtime pay that is 1.5 times more than his regular pay for the hours he works over 40 hours. How much will he get paid if he works 48 hours in one week?

5. Jane works the second shift at a hospital. Her base pay is $13.25 per hour. The hospital gives a shift differential of $1.00 per hour for every hour worked on the second shift. How much will her weekly paycheck be if she works 32 hours?

PTCB EXAM PRACTICE QUESTIONS

1. Which of the following best describes the protection of a patient's privacy (identity and health information)?
   a. Compatibility
   b. Conformity
   c. Compliance
   d. Confidentiality

2. Some patients may feel uncomfortable if the pharmacist or technician stands too close or touches them. Other patients may initiate a handshake or pat on the back. These kinds of differences might be considered:
   a. genetic differences.
   b. cultural differences.
   c. physical differences.
   d. physiological differences.

3. You have a patient who is less than 12 years old. This patient would be categorized as what kind of patient?
   a. geriatric
   b. neonate
   c. pediatric
   d. ambulatory

4. An important communication concept, which refers to the situation, environment, or circumstance in which a message is communicated, is:
   a. projection.
   b. context.
   c. intellectualization.
   d. rationalization.

5. What percentage of Americans 16 years and older have the lowest level of literacy (difficulty using certain reading, writing, and computational skills considered necessary for functioning in everyday life)?
   a. 1–3%
   b. 10–13%
   c. 20–23%
   d. 30–33%

CHAPTER 4
Pharmacy Law and Ethics

After completing Chapter 4 from the textbook, you should be able to:	Related Activity in the Workbook/Lab Manual
1. Classify the various categories of United States law.	Review Questions Lab 4-1
2. List the regulatory agencies that oversee the practice of pharmacy and describe their function(s).	Review Questions, PTCB Exam Practice Questions Lab 4-1
3. Summarize the significant laws and amendments that affect the practice of pharmacy.	Review Questions, PTCB Exam Practice Questions Activity 4-1, Lab 4-1
4. Recognize and use a drug monograph.	Review Questions
5. Define ethics and moral philosophy.	Review Questions Activity 4-1, Activity 4-2
6. List and explain the nine ethical theories.	Review Questions Activity 4-3
7. Summarize the Pharmacy Technician Code of Ethics.	Review Questions Activity 4-3

INTRODUCTION

Federal and state laws, as well as professional ethics, regulate the practice of pharmacy. The regulations on pharmacy practice in the United States have evolved over the past hundred or so years, and their number has increased as legislators responded to demands from citizens to serve and protect the public interest. The government began to take the initiative in regulating pharmacy practice toward the end of the 18th century. Over time, the profession of pharmacy has become increasingly more regulated. In the United States, a professional degree is a requirement for any individual who wishes to practice pharmacy. This requirement was established to protect the public and set minimum standards, so that citizens could rely on pharmacists having at least a standard level of education and competence.

Many of the regulations pertaining to practice as a pharmacy technician are established and enforced by your specific state's board of pharmacy. In general, federal laws govern the manufacturing of pharmaceutical products, and state laws govern the actual dispensing of those products. It is imperative that you familiarize yourself with both the federal laws and your state's laws pertaining to pharmacy practice. In addition, you should fully understand the basic ethical theories and *Code of Ethics for Pharmacy Technicians,* in preparation for ethical dilemmas and questions that will arise in the pharmacy setting.

REVIEW QUESTIONS

Choose the best answer.

1. The quality of being kind or charitable is called:
   a. beneficence.
   b. ethics.
   c. fidelity.
   d. veracity.

2. A drug that has been misleadingly or fraudulently labeled is referred to as:
   a. adulterated.
   b. a felony.
   c. a monograph.
   d. misbranded.

3. A system of principles often associated with a profession is:
   a. civil law.
   b. consequentialism.
   c. ethics.
   d. criminal law.

4. Most laws pertaining to pharmacy were enacted to:
   a. limit the scope and practice of pharmacy.
   b. protect the public interest.
   c. lower the number of drug addicts.
   d. protect drug manufacturers.

5. Which is not a type of law in the United States?
   a. legislative intent
   b. constitutional
   c. government policy
   d. statutes

6. Which set of laws would take priority?
   a. federal
   b. state
   c. municipality
   d. local codes

7. Statutes are laws that are passed by:
   a. the federal government.
   b. state governments.
   c. local governments.
   d. all of the above.

8. Legislative intent is often referred to as:
   a. common law.
   b. case law.
   c. civil law.
   d. all of the above.

9. Regulations:
   a. have the force of law.
   b. are guidelines.
   c. refine laws.
   d. are not connected to laws.

10. Crimes are classified as either ____________ or ____________.
    a. infractions, misdemeanors
    b. infractions, violations
    c. infractions, felonies
    d. felonies, misdemeanors

11. Professional liability insurance is:
    a. currently available only to pharmacists.
    b. available to both pharmacists and pharmacy technicians.
    c. required by most states.
    d. required by the federal government.

12. Which agency/administration is not involved in the practice of pharmacy?
    a. CMS
    b. HIPAA
    c. HCFA
    d. FEMA

13. Which agency/administration is responsible for protecting the privacy of patients?
    a. CLIA
    b. SCHIP
    c. HIPAA
    d. DEA

Match the following.

14. _____ DEA
15. _____ FDA
16. _____ FBI
17. _____ SBOP
18. _____ JCAHO
19. _____ OSHA

a. regulates and registers pharmacy technicians, pharmacists, and pharmacies
b. establishes and enforces standards for healthcare organizations
c. assures the safety, efficacy, and security of drugs
d. regulates the legal trade in controlled drugs
e. the administrator of the DEA reports to this chief
f. assures the safety and health of American workers

Choose the best answer.

20. The Food and Drug Administration was created by the:
    a. Food, Drug and Cosmetic Act of 1938.
    b. Pure Food and Drug Act of 1905.
    c. Controlled Substances Act of 1970.
    d. FBI's need to expand to combat prevalent drug abuse.

21. "A display of written, printed, or graphic matter upon the immediate container of an article" refers to the:
    a. label.
    b. labeling.
    c. package insert.
    d. patient information sheet.

22. Which of the following information is not a labeling requirement for a dispensed prescription?
    a. NDC
    b. serial number (Rx number)
    c. date of fill
    d. prescriber's name

23. Which of the following information is not required to be on the manufacturer's label of a prescription-only drug?
    a. route of administration
    b. name and quantity of active ingredients
    c. date of fill
    d. federal legend

24. Which of the following information is not required to be on the package insert?
    a. dosage
    b. indications and usage
    c. adverse reactions
    d. unique lot or control number

Fill in the blank.

25. The amendment signed in 1951 that required the "federal legend" to be printed on all prescription drugs was ____________.

26. The Kefauver-Harris Amendment, signed in 1962, is also referred to as the ____________.

Match the following.

27. _____ Kefauver-Harris Amendment
28. _____ Pure Food and Drug Act of 1906
29. _____ Food, Drug, and Cosmetic Act
30. _____ Durham-Humphrey Amendment
31. _____ Schedule I
32. _____ Schedule II
33. _____ Schedule III
34. _____ Schedule IV
35. _____ Schedule V
36. _____ DEA Form 224
37. _____ DEA Form 225
38. _____ DEA Form 363
39. _____ DEA Form 222
40. _____ DEA Form 41

a. limits interstate commerce in drugs to those that are safe and effective
b. established "federal legend"
c. focuses on drug manufacturers' accountability for the efficacy, or effectiveness, of drugs
d. neglected to ban unsafe drugs
e. low abuse, limited dependence
f. lowest abuse potential, lowest dependency
g. no accepted medical use, high abuse potential and high dependency risk
h. high potential for abuse and dependency
i. mostly combination drugs, moderate dependency
j. needed to compound narcotics or conduct narcotic treatment
k. used to report lost or stolen C-II drugs
l. needed to order C-II drugs from distributor
m. needed to dispense
n. needed to manufacture or distribute

True or False?

41. The patient's street address or P.O. box number is required on all C-II prescriptions.

    T F

42. C-II prescriptions must be kept separate from all other prescriptions.

    T F

43. All prescription drugs must be distributed in childproof containers.

    T F

Choose the best answer.

44. The first five digits of an NDC number identify which of the following?
    a. drug
    b. manufacturer
    c. package size
    d. distributor

45. Anabolic steroids (except estrogens, progestins, and corticosteroids) are classified in which schedule?
    a. C-I
    b. C-II
    c. C-III
    d. C-IV

46. Ethics is which of the following?
   a. law
   b. religion
   c. morals
   d. none of the above

Match the following.

47. _____ indication
48. _____ warnings
49. _____ contraindications
50. _____ precautions

a. lists types of patient who should not use the drug
b. lists remaining possible side effects
c. specific conditions that the FDA has approved the drug to treat
d. serious side effects and what to do

Match the following.

51. _____ fidelity
52. _____ beneficence
53. _____ veracity
54. _____ justice
55. _____ autonomy
56. _____ ethics of care
57. _____ rights-based ethics
58. _____ principle-based ethics
59. _____ virtues-based ethics

a. acting with fairness or equity
b. acting with self-reliance
c. bringing about good
d. telling the truth
e. keeping a promise
f. the idealization of morals
g. more personal approach
h. democratic view of individuals
i. focus on kindness, tact, etc.

PHARMACY CALCULATION PROBLEMS

Calculate the following.

1. A prescription states that the patient is to take one tablet by mouth twice daily for 10 days. How many tablets will you need to dispense for a 10-day supply?

2. An antibiotic suspension is dispensed in a 150 mL bottle. If the patient takes 5 mL by mouth three times a day, how many days will the antibiotic last?

3. A customer gives herself one enoxaparin injection every day. If enoxaparin comes in a 10-count box (a box of 10 single-dose syringes), how many boxes will the customer need for 30 days?

4. A patient with a chronic pain condition applies one fentanyl patch every 72 hours for pain relief. How often does the patient need to apply a new patch?

5. If the patient in question #4 needs enough patches to last 15 days, how many patches should the pharmacy dispense?

PTCB EXAM PRACTICE QUESTIONS

1. The Omnibus Budget Reconciliation Act (OBRA) requires that pharmacists provide:
   a. childproof containers to all patients.
   b. counseling services to Medicaid patients.
   c. HMO coverage to all patients.
   d. privacy.

2. HIPAA regulations were established to safeguard and maintain patient privacy. In the law, PHI stands for which of the following?
   a. personal health information
   b. protected health information
   c. professional health information
   d. programmed health information

3. In response to incidents of fatal poisoning from liquid sulfanilamide, which of the following laws required proof that new drugs were safe before they could be marketed?
   a. Food and Drug Act of 1906
   b. 1938 Food, Drug, and Cosmetic Act
   c. 1951 Durham-Humphrey Amendment
   d. The Kefauver-Harris Amendment of 1962

4. The Combat Methamphetamine Epidemic Act requires that OTC cold and allergy medications that contain which of the following drugs be kept behind the counter?
   a. antihistamine
   b. methamphetamine
   c. ephedrine and pseudoephedrine
   d. dextromethorphan

5. Which law required childproof packaging for most prescription drugs?
   a. Food, Drug, and Cosmetic Act
   b. Poison Prevention Packaging Act
   c. Durham-Humphrey Amendment
   d. Kefauver-Harris Amendment

ACTIVITY 4-1: Case Study—Legal Matters and Patient Confidentiality

Instructions: Read the following scenarios and then answer the critical thinking questions.

You and your spouse are having dinner out one evening. As usual, you both discuss events from the day at work. Frustrated, you begin sharing with your spouse, "I had this one patient today, Sharon Eckels, who nearly put me over the edge. She came into the pharmacy and handed us her empty bottle for her antipsychotics, and demanded that we refill it right away. Why can't people call ahead before they run completely out?!"

"That's ridiculous," your spouse responds.

It just so happens that Mr. Eckels, a prominent attorney in the community, is having dinner with a client at a nearby table, and they both overhear your comments. Initially embarrassed, Mr. Eckels is now outraged by the breach of patient confidentiality.

1. What, if any, law or regulation was violated by your dinner conversation?

   Well, when the "(privacy of the patient's privacy)" patient's privacy.

2. Do the Eckels have a legitimate lawsuit pertaining to patient confidentiality? Why?

   No. because eventhough Mr. Eckel is attorney they can't just discuss patient's condition in public areas.

3. Could you be liable for your actions? Could the pharmacy be liable for your actions? Explain.

   Yes... Yea.

4. What would have been an appropriate way to express your frustration at dinner?

   It should've been discussed in private in a discrect manner.

ACTIVITY 4-2: Case Study—Medication Errors and Liability

Instructions: Read the following scenario and then answer the critical thinking questions.

Note: Based on an actual event.

A pharmacy technician who worked at the inpatient pharmacy of a children's hospital made an error when preparing an IV bag. Instead of using a prepackaged saline solution containing 0.9% NaCl (salt), the technician prepared an IV bag with a solution that was 23.4 percent NaCl.

The IV was reviewed and verified by the staff pharmacist. Although the technician did raise several questions about the product, it was approved and dispensed for administration. The patient to whom it was given, who was two years old, died three days later.

1. Who is responsible for the medication error: the technician, the pharmacist, or both?

2. Who could be held liable for the medication error: the technician, the pharmacist, or both?

3. What do you think would be an appropriate judgment in this scenario: for the parents of the child, for the technician, for the pharmacist, and for the hospital?

ACTIVITY 4-3: Case Study—Ethical Considerations

Instructions: Read the following scenarios and then answer the critical thinking questions.

Scenario 1

A young man comes into the pharmacy and asks to purchase a box of syringes. When you inquire if he has a prescription for insulin or syringes on file at the pharmacy, he quickly says that he usually fills his prescription at another pharmacy. You also notice that he has not requested a specific size or gauge of syringe. Your intuition tells you that this young man wants to purchase syringes for recreational drug use. If you sell him the syringes, it could be argued that you are enabling his drug use. However, it could also be argued that if you do not sell him the syringes, he will likely still continue to abuse drugs, possibly with dirty or used syringes.

Scenario 2

During the peak of cold and flu season, the manufacturer of one of the best over-the-counter remedies is back-ordered on its products, with an expected delay of six weeks for shipments. You are aware that all the other pharmacies in town are already completely out of stock on this product, but your pharmacy has one package left. An elderly woman comes into the pharmacy, clearly suffering from a nasty cold, to ask if you have any of the medicine available. You promised your next-door-neighbor that you would hold the last package for his family; although they have not yet gotten sick, they want to have the medicine on hand.

1. In scenario 1, would you sell the young man syringes as he is requesting? Why?

___

___

___

___

2. In scenario 2, would you sell the last package of the cold remedy to the elderly woman, or would you reserve it for your neighbor as promised? Why?

___

___

___

___

3. What ethical theory or moral principle discussed in Chapter 4 of the text are you using as the basis of your decision in question #1? Explain.

___

___

___

___

4. What ethical theory or moral principle are you using as the basis of your decision in question #2? Explain.

___

___

___

___

LAB 4-1: Creating a Pharmacy Law Timeline

Objective:

Review and remember the major laws that pertain to the practice of pharmacy in the United States.

Pre-Lab Information:

Review Chapter 4, "Pharmacy Law and Ethics," in your text.

Explanation:

It is important for pharmacy technicians to have an understanding of pharmacy law. Many of our current laws were enacted because of an injury to persons using medications. The progression of laws related to the practice of pharmacy through American history can give you a better perspective on current laws and regulations.

Activity:

Using the following chart, complete the timeline by filling in the correct year in which each law was passed.

Law	Timeline
The Pure Food and Drug Act	1906
The Prescription Drug Marketing Act	1987
The Occupational Safety and Health Act	1970
The Orphan Drug Act	1983
The Medical Device Amendment	1976
The Poison Prevention Packaging Act	1970
The Omnibus Budget Reconciliation Act	1990
The Kefauver-Harris Amendment	1962
The Health Insurance Portability and Accountability Act	1996
The Controlled Substances Act	1970
The Combat Methamphetamine Epidemic Act	2005
The Durham-Humphrey Amendment	1951
The Drug Listing Act	1972
The Anabolic Steroids Act	1990
The Food, Drug, and Cosmetic Act	1938
The Dietary Supplement Health and Education Act	1994
The Drug Price Competition and Patent Term Restoration Act	1984

1. Name four broad categories of law in the United States and provide a brief definition of each.

____

____

____

____

2. What is the difference between criminal and civil law?

____

____

____

____

3. Name six of the regulatory agencies that oversee the practice of pharmacy in the United States and describe their function(s).

____

____

____

____

____

____

CHAPTER 5
Terminology and Abbreviations

After completing Chapter 5 from the textbook, you should be able to:	Related Activity in the Workbook/Lab Manual
1. Identify selected root words used in pharmacy practice.	Review Questions Activity 5-3, Lab 5-1
2. Identify and correctly use selected prefixes and suffixes in conjunction with root words.	Review Questions Activity 5-3, Lab 5-1
3. Recognize and interpret common abbreviations used in pharmacy and medicine.	Review Questions, Pharmacy Calculation Problems, PTCB Exam Practice Questions Activity 5-1, Activity 5-2, Lab 5-1
4. List abbreviations that are considered dangerous and explain why.	Review Questions, PTCB Exam Practice Questions
5. Recognize and list common drug names and their generic equivalents.	Review Questions, PTCB Exam Practice Questions Lab 5-1
6. Recall and define common pharmacy and medical terminology.	Review Questions Activity 5-3, Lab 5-1

INTRODUCTION

To understand the pharmacy industry and profession, you must learn its language, which consists of medical terminology, abbreviations, and drug names. Most medical terms derive from Greek and Latin and consist of a root word, prefix, and/or suffix. It is unlikely that you will remember all the information contained in Chapter 5 of the textbook, but by learning selected roots, prefixes, and suffixes, you will be able to understand words you may have never seen or heard before. Over time, with experience and practice, you will develop a strong working knowledge of medical terminology.

REVIEW QUESTIONS

Match the following.

1. _____ pneum	a. fast
2. _____ arthr	b. abnormal
3. _____ cyst	c. nose
4. _____ my	d. bone
5. _____ oste	e. bladder
6. _____ ectomy	f. lung
7. _____ rhin	g. muscle
8. _____ brady	h. too much
9. _____ dys	i. cell
10. _____ hyper	j. inflammation
11. _____ tachy	k. thirst
12. _____ itis	l. too slow
13. _____ cyte	m. surgical removal
14. _____ dipsia	n. joint
15. _____ intra	o. within

Choose the best answer.

16. The part of a word that helps identify its major meaning is the:

a. prefix.
b. suffix.
c. root.
d. origin.

17. A part of a word that is attached at the beginning of the term is a:

a. prefix.
b. suffix.
c. root.
d. origin.

18. Which of the following are on JCAHO's "do not use" list?

a. qhs
b. SC
c. QOD
d. all of the above

Fill in the blank.

19. ADR is the accepted abbreviation for ____________.

Match the following.

20. _____ blood sugar
21. _____ after meals
22. _____ as needed
23. _____ before meals
24. _____ as directed
25. _____ left ear
26. _____ twice daily
27. _____ intramuscular
28. _____ no known allergies
29. _____ drop
30. _____ milliliter
31. _____ aspirin
32. _____ potassium
33. _____ penicillin
34. _____ iron
35. _____ acetaminophen
36. _____ sodium

a. IM
b. u.d.
c. apap
d. Fe
e. gtt
f. BS
g. NKA
h. pc
i. prn
j. bid
k. ac
l. AS
m. Na
n. ASA
o. K
p. PCN
q. mL

Match the following brand drugs with their generics.

37. _____ Accutane®
38. _____ Zoloft®
39. _____ Flexeril®
40. _____ Toprol XL®
41. _____ Allegra®
42. _____ Zithromax®
43. _____ Inderal®
44. _____ Feldene®
45. _____ Aldactone®
46. _____ Humalog®
47. _____ Coumadin®
48. _____ Lodine®
49. _____ Demerol®
50. _____ Ambien®
51. _____ Fastin®
52. _____ Celebrex®
53. _____ Antivert®
54. _____ Halcion®
55. _____ Lamisil®
56. _____ Aricept®

a. zolpidem tartrate
b. insulin lispro
c. piroxicam
d. meperidine
e. warfarin
f. etodolac
g. propranolol HCl
h. fexofenadine HCl
i. azithromycin
j. clonidine HCl
k. donepezil HCl
l. spirolactone
m. celecoxib
n. meclizine
o. isotretinoin
p. phentermine
q. clarithromycin
r. triazolam
s. valsartan
t. sertraline

57. _____ Catapres
58. _____ Phenergan
59. _____ Diovan
60. _____ Augmentin
61. _____ Plavix
62. _____ Biaxin

u. clopidogrel
v. amoxicillin and clavulanate potassium
w. promethazine HCl
x. metroprolol tartrate
y. terbinafine
z. cyclobenzaprine

PHARMACY CALCULATION PROBLEMS

Calculate the following.

1. A prescription reads: "Cephalexin 500 mg: 1 cap qid × 10d." How many capsules should you dispense?

2. If a patient takes 5 mL of albuterol syrup BID, how many mL should you dispense for a 30-day supply?

3. How many drops of timolol ophthalmic solution is a patient using per day if the instructions read: 2 gtts ou qid?

4. A prescription reads: "Azithromycin 250 mg: Take two tablets by mouth once daily for the first day, then one tablet on days 2–5." How many tablets will you dispense?

5. A bottle of fluticasone nasal spray contains 120 metered doses. If the directions state: "Use 2 sprays in each nostril QD," how many days will the spray last?

PTCB EXAM PRACTICE QUESTIONS

1. Tobrex ophthalmic ung refers to:
   a. an ointment used for the eye.
   b. a solution used for the eye.
   c. a topical ointment for external use only.
   d. an ointment used for the ear.

2. If a medication is to be taken a.c., it should be taken:
   a. in the morning.
   b. around the clock.
   c. after meals.
   d. before meals.

3. Which of the following abbreviations is considered acceptable for use when writing medication orders?
   a. Q.D.
   b. Q.O.D.
   c. Q.I.D.
   d. U

4. What is the generic name for the drug Zantac?
   a. cimetidine
   b. ranitidine
   c. zidovudine
   d. cytarabine

5. What healthcare accreditation organization has created a list of "do not use" abbreviations?
   a. APHA
   b. APA
   c. NABP
   d. JCAHO

ACTIVITY 5-1: Case Study—Lost in Translation

Instructions: Read the following scenarios and then answer the critical thinking questions provided.

Scenario 1

A patient brings in a new prescription for Glucophage XR 500 mg. When you are processing the prescription into the pharmacy computer, you quickly select Glucophage 500 mg from the drop-down list of medications as you scroll down. The prescription is filled and dispensed, as neither you nor the pharmacist notice that the prescription was written for Glucophage XR (extended release) as opposed to Glucophage.

Scenario 2

When writing up a compounding formula sheet, you put down that .5 mg of active ingredient is to be used per dose. The following month, however, another technician is reviewing the formula to prepare the patient's refill. The refill is prepared using 5 mg of active ingredient per dose, as opposed to 0.5 mg.

1. What translation error occurred in Scenario 1?

____

____

____

____

2. What effect will the error in Scenario 1 have?

____

____

____

____

3. What translation error occurred in Scenario 2?

____

____

____

____

4. What effect will the error in Scenario 2 have?

____

____

____

____

5. Who is responsible for the mistake in Scenario 2? How could it most easily have been avoided?

____

____

____

____

6. What can you do to ensure that these types of errors are avoided?

____

____

____

____

ACTIVITY 5-2: Practice with Abbreviations

For each of the following, write the meaning next to the abbreviation.

1. p ____________
2. pm ____________
3. ad lib ____________
4. ac ____________
5. po ____________
6. DAW ____________
7. hr ____________
8. bid ____________
9. u.d. ____________
10. qd ____________
11. s ____________
12. AU ____________
13. prn ____________
14. qw ____________
15. WA ____________
16. disp. ____________
17. fl. ____________
18. ped ____________
19. OTC ____________
20. NKA ____________

Now, write the appropriate abbreviation after its meaning.

21. suppository ____________
22. vitamin ____________
23. syrup ____________
24. water ____________
25. buccal ____________
26. intravenous ____________
27. by mouth ____________
28. nasal ____________
29. otic ____________
30. drops ____________

ACTIVITY 5-3: Defining Medical Terms

Using a medical dictionary, your text, or an online medical resource, define the following medical terms. Then, break the term into its word parts and define each word part as well.

1. gynecologist
   Definition: ______________________________
   Word parts: ______________________________
2. rhinoplasty
   Definition: ______________________________
   Word parts: ______________________________
3. epigastric
   Definition: ______________________________
   Word parts: ______________________________
4. arthritis
   Definition: ______________________________
   Word parts: ______________________________
5. abduction
   Definition: ______________________________
   Word parts: ______________________________
6. erythrocytes
   Definition: ______________________________
   Word parts: ______________________________
7. leukocytes
   Definition: ______________________________
   Word parts: ______________________________
8. arteriosclerosis
   Definition: ______________________________
   Word parts: ______________________________

LAB 5-1: Translating a Medical Record

Objective:

Reinforce your knowledge of terminology and abbreviations by completing this exercise based on a medical record entry.

Pre-Lab Information:

Review Chapter 5, "Terminology and Abbreviations," in your text.

Explanation:

It is important for pharmacy technicians to have a basic understanding of the language used in medicine. This exercise will help you gain experience by "translating" a medical record entry.

Activity:

Read the following pharmacist SOAP (Subjective, Objective, Assessment, Plan) note from a patient's pharmacist consultation and answer questions related to the content, using your knowledge of terminology and abbreviations.

S:	67 yo BF with Hx of arthritis, obesity, hyperlipidemia, hypertension. Several questions about medications and improving health status.	
O:	Type 2 DM	Morning BS 130–155+; does not test routinely, A1c 8.5% (6 mo ago)
	HTN	155/95 on ramipril 10 mg bid
	Hyperlipidemia	TC 219, LDL 143, TRG 185 (6 mo ago) on simvastatin 20 mg once daily
	Obesity	5′9″ / 230 lb, BMI 34
	RA	Knee and hip pain with exercise, APAP prn only
	SCr	1.6 (6 mo ago)
	Vitals	P 78, R 19
		Not taking ASA for CVD prevention
A:	Diabetes	Poor compliance diet/meal planning; poor understanding of BS testing; above goal of A1c <7%
	HTN	Above goal of BP 125/80 with Tx
	Hyperlipidemia	Above goal of LDL ≤ 100 with Tx
	Obesity	Above goal, 25 lb gain over last 6 mo, min exercise frequency; Initial goal 10% weight loss at 1–2 lb/wk (23 lb in 4 mo)
	RA	Still not well controlled

P:	Improve medication adherence and health outcomes. • HTN: Recommended changing ramipril 10 mg bid to lisinopril/HCTZ 20/12.5 bid • Hyperlipidemia: Recommended increasing simvastatin from 20 mg to 40 mg once daily • RA: Recommended diclofenac XR 100 mg once daily for RA • Cardiovascular health: Recommended adding lo-dose ASA daily • Provided and instructed pt with daily BS monitoring log • Provided and instructed pt with personal health tracking tool • Reviewed "ADA Dietary Guidelines" and shopping/meal planner guide • Suggested pt walk 30–60 min/day • Schedule for 90-day F/U appt. • Schedule for repeat of the following labs 2 weeks prior to 90-day FU appt: SCr, fasting lipid profile, A1c, BG

Duration of appt: 45 minutes

Pharmacist's signature: ______________________________

Questions:

1. What does the abbreviation Hx mean?
____
____

2. What does APAP prn mean?
____
____

3. In the "Objective" section, which drug (generic and brand name) did the patient take to control cholesterol?
____
____

4. In the "Objective" section, which drug (generic and brand name) did the patient take to control blood pressure?
____
____

5. What does the abbreviation BS mean?
____
____

6. What does the abbreviation HTN mean?

____

____

7. In the "Plan" section, what drug (generic and brand) did the pharmacist recommend changing for the patient's HTN?

____

____

8. In the "Plan" section, what does the abbreviation ASA mean?

____

____

CHAPTER 6

Retail Pharmacy

After completing Chapter 6 from the textbook, you should be able to:	Related Activity in the Workbook/Lab Manual
1. Explain the ambulatory pharmacy practice setting.	Review Questions
2. Describe the two main types of retail pharmacies.	Review Questions
3. List the various staff positions in retail pharmacies.	Review Questions Activity 6-4
4. Describe the typical work environment of a retail pharmacy.	Review Questions
5. Discuss the two agencies that regulate retail pharmacy practice.	Review Questions, PTCB Exam Practice Questions
6. List the legal requirements of a prescription medication order.	Review Questions, PTCB Exam Practice Questions Activity 6-3, Lab 6-1
7. Describe the different ways prescriptions arrive at a retail pharmacy.	Review Questions Activity 6-1
8. List the steps required for a prescription to be filled.	Review Questions, PTCB Exam Practice Questions Activity 6-1
9. Discuss the various job duties of technicians in retail pharmacies.	Review Questions Activity 6-1, Activity 6-3, Activity 6-4, Lab 6-1, Lab 6-2
10. Discuss the importance of confidentiality for personal health information.	Review Questions, PTCB Exam Practice Questions Activity 6-2

INTRODUCTION

The two main types of pharmacy practice are ambulatory and institutional. An institutional pharmacy is located on the site of the patients' residence; pharmacies within hospitals, nursing homes, hospices, and long-term care facilities are examples. Most other pharmacies fall into the category of ambulatory. Examples of ambulatory settings, which are usually called *community-based* or *retail pharmacies,* are privately owned, chain, and franchise pharmacies, as well as clinics. Retail pharmacy is the largest category of pharmacy in the United States. These types of pharmacies serve the community in which they are located.

The staff at a retail pharmacy includes the pharmacist in charge (PIC), pharmacy manager, staff pharmacists, pharmacy technicians, and, in many cases, pharmacy clerks. It is a fast-paced work environment where pharmacy professionals interact with patients face to face. Pharmacy technicians have numerous job responsibilities, from taking care of inventory orders, rotations, returns, and billing to counting, measuring, filling, and labeling. In the retail environment, you may also help patients find OTC medications or lead them to the pharmacist for counseling, to name only a few of your daily tasks. In ambulatory pharmacy, every day is another opportunity to serve the community.

REVIEW QUESTIONS

Match the following.

1. _____ chain pharmacy
2. _____ franchise pharmacy
3. _____ neighborhood pharmacy
4. _____ retail pharmacy

a. name for all kinds of ambulatory pharmacies
b. privately owned small pharmacy
c. corporately owned, multiple-site pharmacy
d. ambulatory, multiple-site pharmacy

Fill in the blanks.

5. The process of transmitting a prescription electronically to the proper insurance carrier for approval is called _____________.
6. The code DAW, when written by the prescriber, means _____________.
7. An electronic record stored in the pharmacy computer system detailing the patient's personal and billing information, prescription records, and medical conditions is known as a/an _____________.
8. When the patients reside where the medication is kept, the pharmacy there is described as a/an _____________ pharmacy.
9. The agency that registers and regulates retail pharmacy facilities, pharmacists, and pharmacy technicians, as well as the practice of pharmacy, is known as _____________.
10. The _____________ conducts inspections to ensure compliance with its guidelines and also approves reimbursement for Medicare and Medicaid.

True or False?

11. Retail pharmacy practice allows a more hands-on approach.

    T F

12. The term "PharmD" is used to designate a Director of Pharmacy.

    T F

13. Pregnancy tests can be obtained only with a prescription.

T F

14. Any OTC product may be kept behind the counter if the pharmacist chooses.

T F

Choose the best answer.

15. Which of the following is not an approved prescriber?
    a. DDS
    b. PA
    c. DVM
    d. RN

16. Which of the following is a valid DEA number for Dr. Rebecca Carey?
    a. AC5932764
    b. BC8162753
    c. BC3791250
    d. AC79131591

17. A C-III prescription may be refilled:
    a. 6 times.
    b. 0 times.
    c. for six months from the date it was written.
    d. for one year from the date it was first filled.

18. Which of the following is not required on a prescription?
    a. route of administration
    b. patient's age
    c. strength of drug
    d. prescriber's signature

19. The prescriber wrote Mr. Mallory's prescription for Synthroid® on 12/14/2008 with prn refills. Mr. Mallory had the prescription filled for the first time on 3/09/09. He may continue receiving monthly refills until:
    a. 12/14/2009.
    b. 12/14/2008.
    c. 03/09/2010.
    d. 03/09/2009.

20. The second group of numbers in an NDC code signifies:
    a. package size.
    b. manufacturer.
    c. drug, strength, and form.
    d. cost (AWP).

21. Once a medication has left the pharmacy counter, it may:
    a. not be returned for resale.
    b. not be returned for a refund.
    c. not be returned for resale or refund.
    d. be refunded and/or resold if the pharmacist allows.

22. Most pharmacies and insurance providers require a prescription to be ____________ used before it may be refilled.
    a. 50%
    b. 90%
    c. 75%
    d. 100%

23. Most states restrict controlled medications with refills:
    a. to a maximum of one transfer.
    b. to zero transfers; controlled substances may not be refilled.
    c. so that all refills written by the prescriber may be transferred.
    d. to a maximum of three refills that are transferred.

24. It is not a technician's responsibility to:
   a. verify the information in a patient's profile.
   b. counsel a patient on the use of a medication.
   c. double-count a controlled medication for accuracy.
   d. contact an insurance provider on behalf of a patient.

25. When Mrs. Rigby asked to have her Lunesta® prescription transferred from across town, the technician should have:
   a. explained to her that controlled medications cannot be transferred.
   b. informed her that the sending pharmacy has to call.
   c. checked her profile to see if the prescription had been transferred before and had refills remaining.
   d. warned her it may take up to 24 hours to complete the transfer.

PHARMACY CALCULATION PROBLEMS

Calculate the following.

1. The directions for a prescription cough medicine state: Take 5 ml po q4h prn. If the patient takes the maximum daily amount, how long will a 120 mL bottle last?

2. If the sig states "2 tabs po q hs," how many tablets will you need to dispense to last for 28 days?

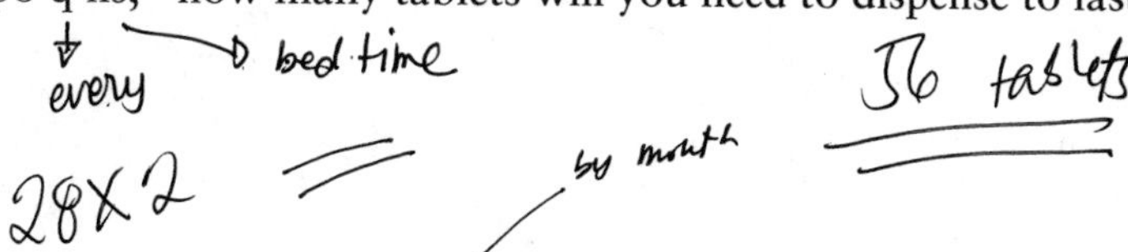

3. If a patient is taking tetracycline 250 mg caps po QID, how many capsules are needed for a 30-day supply?

4. Jill is compounding a prescription that requires $\frac{3}{4}$ oz. of hydrocortisone 1% cream, $\frac{1}{4}$ oz. nystatin cream, and $\frac{1}{4}$ oz. of clotrimazole 1% cream. How many ounces will be in the finished product?

5. A technician receives a prescription for a controlled substance. The prescription is from out of state and the technician is unfamiliar with the physician and the customer. The DEA number for the physician is AG8642123. Is this a fraudulent prescription?

PTCB EXAM PRACTICE QUESTIONS

1. Which organization oversees the practice of community pharmacies in the United States?
   a. FDA
   b. DEA
   c. SBOP
   d. APHA

2. In the following number, NDC 51285-601-05, the first set (51285) represents which of the following?
   a. drug name
   b. manufacturer
   c. dosage form
   d. capsule size

3. How many times can you refill a prescription for Viagra®?
   a. As many times as indicated by the prescriber.
   b. As many times as indicated by the prescriber within one year from the date the prescription was written.
   c. Six times within six months.
   d. None.

4. Which law provides for protection of patient confidentiality?
   a. HIPAA
   b. JCAHO
   c. OSHA
   d. CSA

5. What is online adjudication?
   a. The process of transmitting prescription information electronically to the proper insurance company or third-party payor for approval and billing.
   b. The process of transmitting orders for controlled drugs.
   c. The process of transferring a prescription to another pharmacy.
   d. The process of receiving a fax from a physician's office.

ACTIVITY 6-1: Prescription Translation Worksheet

Review each of the following five prescriptions, then translate the information contained in each one.

Rx #1

Towne Center Family Medicine
40 Towne Center Drive
Pleasantville, Texas 77248-0124
Phone 281-555-0134 Fax 281-555-0125

James L. Brook, MD BB1234563	Rebecca Smith, MD AS1234563	Walter Roberts, MD AR1234563
Sharon Ortiz, NP	Beth Matthews, NP	Terri King, NP

Name Melvin Brooks Age______

Address______ Date Nov 21

℞

Isordol 10 mg

#60

T po bid

Refill______times

[signature]

Signature

A generically equivalent drug product may be dispensed unless the practitioner hand writes the words 'Brand Necessary' or 'Brand Medically Necessary' on the face of the prescription. 6HUR133050

1. Patient name: Melvin Brooks
2. Prescriber: Sharon Ortiz, NP
3. Drug name and strength: Isordol / 10 mg
4. Is generic substitution permitted? yea
5. Quantity to dispense: 60
6. Directions: take 1 tablet by mouth two times daily
7. Refills authorized: –

Rx #2

Towne Center Family Medicine
40 Towne Center Drive
Pleasantville, Texas 77248-0124
Phone 281-555-0134 Fax 281-555-0125

James L. Brook, MD BB1234563	Rebecca Smith, MD AS1234563	Walter Roberts, MD AR1234563
Sharon Ortiz, NP	Beth Matthews, NP	Terri King, NP

Name Beth Andrews Age

Address Date 03/12

℞

Allegra 60mg

#60

T po Bid

Refill 2 times

Signature

A generically equivalent drug product may be dispensed unless the practitioner hand writes the words 'Brand Necessary' or 'Brand Medically Necessary' on the face of the prescription.

6HUR133050

1. Patient name: Beth Andrews
2. Prescriber: James Brook
3. Drug name and strength: Allegra 60 mg
4. Is generic substitution permitted? yes
5. Quantity to dispense: 60
6. Directions: Take one tablet by mouth two times daily
7. Refills authorized: 2

Rx #3

Towne Center Family Medicine
40 Towne Center Drive
Pleasantville, Texas 77248-0124
Phone 281-555-0134 Fax 281-555-0125

James L. Brook, MD BB1234563	Rebecca Smith, MD AS1234563	Walter Roberts, MD AR1234563
Sharon Ortiz, NP	Beth Matthews, NP	Terri King, NP

Name Stephanie Ruiz Age ____

Address ____ Date March 12

℞

Azelex 30g

#1

U-mal UD

Refill 3 times

Becky Smith
Signature

A generically equivalent drug product may be dispensed unless the practitioner hand writes the words 'Brand Necessary' or 'Brand Medically Necessary' on the face of the prescription.

6HUR133050

1. Patient name: Stephanie Ruiz
2. Prescriber: Rebecca Smith
3. Drug name and strength: Azelex
4. Is generic substitution permitted? yes
5. Quantity to dispense: 1
6. Directions: use 1 tablet as directed
7. Refills authorized: 3

ACTIVITY 6-2: Case Study—Privacy/HIPAA

Instructions: Read the following scenario and then answer the critical thinking questions.

A remodel of the workspace at the retail pharmacy in which you work has finally begun. Many people were involved in the design planning, including various construction personnel. However, no one from the pharmacy itself was included on the planning committee. Weeks pass, and it appears that the newly remodeled pharmacy will allow a more efficient use of space.

The remodel is completed on a Friday, and everyone returns to work on Monday excited to see the new space. Almost immediately, everyone notices that the redesigned space lacks an adequate area for patient counseling. HIPAA mandates that every pharmacy have a patient counseling area.

The pharmacy does not close down while this space is added, but instead remains open for business, and pharmacy personnel are asked to "work around" the inconvenience. You are told that the counseling area will be in place after two more weeks of construction. In the meantime, it seems almost impossible to find a private space to counsel patients.

1. What are some creative ways in which the pharmacy could assure patient privacy during counseling until construction is complete?

   ____

   ____

   ____

   ____

2. What effect might this inconvenience have on the pharmacy workload, in terms of time?

   ____

   ____

   ____

   ____

3. Describe what a HIPAA-compliant counseling area, which protects patient privacy, might look like or include.

   ____

   ____

   ____

   ____

ACTIVITY 6-3: Case Study—Biases

Instructions: Read the following scenario and then answer the critical thinking questions.

A gangly, unkempt, middle-aged man with a slightly offensive odor presents a prescription at your pharmacy for hydrocodone bitartrate 5 mg/acetaminophen 500 mg #120 to be taken twice daily as needed for pain. He attempts to rush you through the process, talking excessively and stating that he should be getting more than what was prescribed. His actions make you suspicious, in that he appears nervous, is constantly looking around, and becomes increasingly agitated with each question you ask, such as his address and phone number. It appears that the amount of tablets may have been altered, but you are not quite certain, as this provider's writing is not very legible.

The man becomes more and more uncooperative as you try to gain the information you need to process the prescription, but finally you have everything you need. You have been trained to notice things that may raise questions as to the validity of prescriptions and feel that this may be one such situation. You bring this to the attention of the pharmacist in charge, who in turn calls to verify the prescription. It turns out that the prescription is legitimate and the patient has some mental health issues.

1. What were some factors in this scene that made the technician suspect that this might be a fraudulent prescription?

   ____

   ____

   ____

   ____

2. Can you identify any communication barriers present with this type of patient?

   ____

   ____

   ____

   ____

3. Do you think that the way the patient was dressed or acted contributed to the assessment that his might be a fraudulent prescription?

   ____

   ____

   ____

   ____

ACTIVITY 6-4: Case Study—Patient Requests Recommendations

Instructions: Read the following scenario and then answer the critical thinking questions.

Mrs. Hornbuckle, with her 4-year-old daughter in tow, approaches the pharmacy counter and requests some assistance in locating the Children's Tylenol Liquid. You are the only person available, and state that it is located on aisle 6 toward the back of the store; you then offer to show her to the area. Mrs. Hornbuckle accepts your offer and the three of you head to aisle 6.

You point out the Children's Tylenol Liquid section, but before you can walk away, Mrs. Hornbuckle begins asking questions about the wide array of Tylenol liquid preparations. She states that her daughter has a really bad cough and wants to know which one works best, the grape- or the cherry-flavored. Meanwhile, she is picking up boxes and reading the information on the back.

You explain that a pharmacist could answer any questions she may have about the medicines. With a frustrated sigh, she says, "Forget it," and starts to walk out in a huff, obviously upset that you were not able to answer the questions yourself.

1. Why might Mrs. Hornbuckle have felt that you could (and should) have answered her questions about medications?

2. Do you think pharmacy technicians should identify themselves as such, or would it matter to the general public, who may not know the difference between pharmacy technicians and pharmacists?

3. How would you explain to a patient/customer, in an understanding way, your limited authority as a pharmacy technician?

LAB 6-1: Checking a Prescription for Completeness

Objective:

Interpret some sample prescriptions, identify their key components, and determine if the prescriptions contain all the necessary information.

Pre-Lab Information:

Review Tables 5-4, 5-5, 5-6, and 5-7 from Chapter 5 of your textbook to refamiliarize yourself with various medical terms and abbreviations.

Explanation:

Many times a legitimate prescription lacks some of the information required for processing. This exercise will help you review the key components of a prescription, practice translating prescriptions, and identify potential missing information.

Activity:

Four prescriptions have been dropped off at the pharmacy to be filled. The first step is to put the data from the prescriptions into the computer. Translate the prescription, note all key points that must be printed on the labels, and determine if the prescriptions contain all the information needed for processing.

Dr. L. MacCoy
1234 Enterprise Dr
San Francisco, CA 00000
800-555-1234

Name *Jill Johnson* Age ______

Address *79 Holiday Rd* Date *06/08/08*

℞

Metoprolol tablets

#60

Sig: 1 po bid

Refill *5* times

L. MacCoy

Signature

A generically equivalent drug product may be dispensed unless the practitioner hand writes the words 'Brand Necessary' or 'Brand Medically Necessary' on the face of the prescription.

6HUR133050

1. Does the information seem correct on the prescription for Jill Johnson? How would you translate the instructions for the prescription label? Is anything missing from this prescription?

yes.
Take 1 tablet by mouth four times daily
yes. (the name of the prescriber) no.

Dr. Fillmore McGraw
100 Hollywood Blvd.
Los Angeles, CA 00000
(800) 123-4567

Name Britanny Spires Age ______
Address 6002 Hillside Place Date 07/02/08

℞

Xanax 0.25 mg tablet

Sig: 1 po tid prn anxiety

Refill 0 times

Fillmore McGraw
Signature

A generically equivalent drug product may be dispensed unless the practitioner hand writes the words 'Brand Necessary' or 'Brand Medically Necessary' on the face of the prescription. 6HUR133050

2. Does the information seem correct on the prescription for Britanny Spires? How would you translate the instructions for the prescription label? Is anything missing from this prescription?

yes
Take 1 tablet by mouth three times daily as needed
for anxiety (yes, the prescribers name.) no

Elsie Kumar, MD
4605 Lakeshore Drive
Chicago, IL 00000
(819) 555-1111

Name Sandy Deitz Age

Address 123 Laramy Ct Date 05/14/08

℞

Sig: Promethazine 25 mg

1 q4-6hr prn nausea

Refill 0 times

Elsie Kumar, MD
Signature

A generically equivalent drug product may be dispensed unless the practitioner hand writes the words 'Brand Necessary' or 'Brand Medically Necessary' on the face of the prescription.

6HUR133050

3. Does the information seem correct on the prescription for Sandy Deitz? How would you translate the instructions for the prescription label? Is anything missing from this prescription?

(~~yes~~) No.

Take 1 Promethazine one time every 6 hours for nausea. (prescriber) No.

Timothy Stiles, DDS
65 Main St.
Davenport, IA 00000
(563) 111-2222

Name Jeremy Jacobsen Age

Address 455 Brady Street Date 7/25/08

℞

Amoxicillin 500mg

Sig: 1 po TID X 10 days

Refill 0 times

Signature

A generically equivalent drug product may be dispensed unless the practitioner hand writes the words 'Brand Necessary' or 'Brand Medically Necessary' on the face of the prescription.

6HUR133050

4. Does the information seem correct on the prescription for Jeremy Jacobsen? How would you translate the instructions for the prescription label? How many capsules will be needed to fill this prescription? Is anything missing from this prescription?

yes.
take 1 tablet 3 times daily every 10 days. 30.
no.

LAB 6-2: Counting Oral Medication in a Community Pharmacy Setting

Objective:

To demonstrate the ability to count oral medications manually and gain experience with cleaning procedures in the pharmacy.

Pre-Lab Information:

- Review Chapter 6, "Retail Pharmacy," in the textbook.
- Gather the following supplies:
  - Pill counting tray and spatula
  - Large bag of M&Ms®, Skittles®, or other small-sized hard candy
  - Prescription vials, plastic sandwich bags, or other containers for the "tablets"
  - Isopropyl alcohol (70%)

Explanation:

This exercise will give you the opportunity to practice counting "tablets" manually. In the pharmacy, tablets are generally counted in increments of five, using a pill counting tray and spatula on a clean, clutter-free counter. It requires practice to feel confident and efficient in counting tablets by fives, so until you gain experience, remember to count tablets twice before giving them to the "pharmacist."

Activity:

Part 1

For this first exercise, you will count 15 tablets.

1. Prepare a clean, clutter-free work surface, and then place a clean pill counting tray and spatula in front of you.
2. Pour a portion of your "tablets" into the counting tray, then open the lid of the pour compartment.
3. Begin counting the "tablets" in increments of five, using the counting spatula. Slide each group of five into the pour compartment of your tray. Count by fives until you reach fifteen tablets, then close the lid of the pour compartment.
4. Return any unused "tablets" that are still in your counting tray to their container or bag.
5. Select a prescription vial and place it on the counter next to the counting tray.
6. Pour the tablets you counted into the vial.
7. Now pour the tablets you counted back into your counting tray and count them again to make sure you have 15.
8. Repeat step 6. Then place the lid on the vial.

Part 2

For this next exercise, you will use the materials from the previous activity to prepare the following "prescriptions" for "dispensing."

1. Ibuprofen [M&Ms] 800 mg

   Sig: 1 tab tid x 10 days

   Count the correct number of "tablets" required to fill this prescription.

2. M&Mcycline 320 mg tabs

   Sig: 1 tab qid x 5 days

   Count the correct number of "tablets" required to fill this prescription.

3. M&Mnisone 20 mg tabs

   Sig: 1 tab qid x 2 days; 1 tab tid x 2 days; then 1 tab daily x 2 days

   Count the correct number of "tablets" required to fill this prescription.

Feel free to continue counting until all of the tablets are "gone."

Part 3

To complete this lab activity, clean your materials and work area using a disinfectant solution of water and 70% isopropyl alcohol. Spray the solution on the counting tray and spatula, then wipe them with a paper towel and return them to the shelf or appropriate storage location. Then, spray the counter with the solution and wipe the counter down.

CHAPTER 7
Health-System Pharmacy

After completing Chapter 7 from the textbook, you should be able to:	Related Activity in the Workbook/Lab Manual
1. Describe the health-system pharmacy practice setting.	Review Questions, PTCB Exam Practice Questions
2. Describe the advantages of a unit-dose system.	Review Questions, PTCB Exam Practice Questions
3. List the necessary components of a medication order.	Review Questions Activity 7-1, Lab 7-1
4. Compare the duties of a technician with those of a pharmacist in accepting a medication order in a health-system setting.	Review Questions Activity 7-1
5. Compare centralized and decentralized unit-dose systems.	Review Questions
6. Compare the duties of a technician with those of a pharmacist in filling a medication order in a health-system setting.	Review Questions Activity 7-1, Lab 7-1
7. Define the tasks pharmacy technicians perform in health-system settings.	Review Questions Activity 7-1, Lab 7-1

INTRODUCTION

A health-system pharmacy, also called an *institutional pharmacy,* is designed to serve patients who live onsite. Examples of facilities that might include an institutional pharmacy are long-term care facilities, nursing homes, hospitals, correctional facilities, and hospices. Regardless of the type of facility, the onsite pharmacy is responsible for all patients' medications; pharmacy staff must ensure that drug therapies are appropriate, effective, and safe. The health-system pharmacist also identifies, resolves, and prevents medication-related problems. As a pharmacy technician working in this setting, you must understand the policies and procedures of your institution, as well as state and federal laws. In addition to filling prescriptions and medication orders, you might also work with several distribution systems, repackage bulk medications for floors and patient care areas, use unit-dose and automatic dispensing systems, and handle sterile products.

REVIEW QUESTIONS

Match the following.

1. _____ blister packs
2. _____ decentralized pharmacy system
3. _____ centralized pharmacy system
4. _____ emergency medication orders
5. _____ floor stock
6. _____ POE system
7. _____ unit dose
8. _____ STAT order
9. _____ standing order
10. _____ patient prescription stock system
11. _____ PRN order

a. a specific order required to respond to a medical emergency
b. medication order that takes priority over other orders and requests
c. orders are reviewed, prepared, verified, and delivered to the patient
d. allows prescribers to enter orders directly into the pharmacy computer system
e. scheduled order to be administered throughout the day
f. consists of central, inpatient, outpatient, and satellite pharmacies
g. unit-dose packages
h. all pharmacy-related services are performed in one location
i. order used only as necessary
j. medication order is filled for no more than a 24-hour period
k. medications stored on the same floor where patients' rooms are, for patient distribution

Choose the best answer.

12. A licensed individual who is trained to examine patients, diagnose illnesses, and prescribe/administer medication is a:
    a. doctor of medicine (MD).
    b. doctor of osteopathy (DO).
    c. licensed nursing assistant (LPA).
    d. licensed practical nurse (LPN).

13. An individual who is licensed to provide basic care, such as administering medication under the supervision of an RN, is a:
    a. doctor of medicine (MD).
    b. doctor of osteopathy (DO).
    c. licensed nursing assistant (LPA).
    d. licensed practical nurse (LPN).

14. An individual who is registered to assist physicians with specific procedures, administer medication, and provide patient care is a:
    a. licensed practical nurse (LPN).
    b. licensed nursing assistant (LNA).
    c. registered nurse (RN).
    d. nurse practitioner (NP).

15. An individual who is certified to assist RNs and LPNs in providing patient care, but is not permitted to administer medication, is a:
    a. licensed practical nurse (LPN).
    b. licensed nursing assistant (LNA).
    c. registered nurse (RN).
    d. nurse practitioner (NP).

16. An individual who is licensed to work closely with a physician in providing patient care, typically under the supervision of a physician, is a:
    a. licensed practical nurse (LPN).
    b. licensed nursing assistant (LNA).
    c. registered nurse (RN).
    d. nurse practitioner (NP).

17. A licensed individual, who is trained to coordinate patient care under the supervision of a medical or osteopathic doctor, is a:
   a. licensed practical nurse (LPN).
   b. licensed nursing assistant (LNA).
   c. physician's assistant (PA).
   d. nurse practitioner (NP).

18. A pharmacy that provides services to onsite patients 24 hours a day, 365 days each year, is called a:
   a. mail order pharmacy.
   b. health-system pharmacy.
   c. community pharmacy.
   d. all of the above.

19. The American Hospital Association (AHA) categorizes hospitals as community-based, federal government, psychiatric, long-term care, or institutional hospital units. Which represent 85% of the total number of registered hospitals?
   a. community-based
   b. federal government
   c. long-term care
   d. psychiatric

Match the following organizations/agencies/regulations to their area of influence.

20. _____ HIPAA
21. _____ OBRA
22. _____ CMS
23. _____ SCHIP
24. _____ DPH
25. _____ CLIA

a. laboratories
b. children
c. privacy
d. counseling
e. regulates hospitals
f. Medicare/Medicaid

PHARMACY CALCULATION PROBLEMS

Calculate the following.

1. A hospitalized patient needs a 24-hour supply of sucralfate 1 gm tablets. How many tablets will be dispensed if the patient takes it qid? 4 times daily

2. A patient on the infectious disease floor takes 10 mL of levofloxacin syrup bid. If the product is only available as a 5 mL unit-dose oral syringe, how many syringes will the patient need for a 24-hour supply?

3. A technician is checking floor stock on one of the nursing units. She notices that the floor has five acetaminophen 325 mg tablets left, but their par level is 20. How many tablets should the technician restock?

4. While checking a crash cart tray that was recently used for a code, Bill finds that there are two epinephrine syringes left in the tray. When the tray is fully stocked, it contains 12 epinephrine syringes. How many syringes should be restocked in the tray?

5. Karen is repackaging cyanocobalamin 1,000 mcg tablets into unit dosages on 2/16/08. The manufacturer's expiration date for the product is 12/09. What expiration date should Karen assign to the repackaged medication?

PTCB EXAM PRACTICE QUESTIONS

1. Which of the following healthcare practitioners is not considered a prescriber?
   a. medical doctor (MD)
   b. physician assistant (PA)
   c. nurse practitioner (NP)
   d. certified nursing assistant (CNA)

2. A unit dose is a:
   a. package that contains all noncontrolled medications for a given day.
   b. package that contains all medications for a given day
   c. controlled substance.
   d. package that contains the amount of medication for one dose.

3. Which of the following allows a patient to receive medications on an as-needed basis?
   a. STAT order
   b. standing order
   c. parenteral
   d. PRN order

4. Nurses track medication administration on a/an:
   a. PCU.
   b. PRN.
   c. STAT.
   d. MAR.

5. In the health-system setting, needles and other items that can cut or puncture the skin should be thrown away in:
   a. MSDS.
   b. designated sharps containers.
   c. red garbage bags.
   d. regular garbage cans.

ACTIVITY 7-1: Medication Order Translation Worksheet

Review and translate each of the medication orders provided below.

Medication Order #1

PHYSICIAN'S ORDER WORKSHEET

NOTE: ***Person initiating entry should write legibly, date the form using (Mo/Day/Yr.), enter time, sign, and indicate their title.***

USE BALL POINT PEN (PRESS FIRMLY)

45671001 311A
Eckels, Ruby G.
04-10-1943

Dr. C. Thomsen

Date	Time	Treatment
10/18	4:30	Dilaudid 0.5 mg IV inject q 3 h (every hour) prn (as needed) pain (for pain)
		②

PHYSICIAN'S ORDER WORKSHEET | Distribution: (Original) Medical Record Copy (Plies 3, 2, & 1) Pharmacy | **T-5**

1. Patient name: Ruby Fields
2. Prescriber: ______
3. Drug name and strength: Dilaudid
4. Directions: ______

Medication Order #2

PHYSICIAN'S ORDER WORKSHEET

NOTE: ***Person initiating entry should write legibly, date the form using (Mo/Day/Yr.), enter time, sign, and indicate their title.***

USE BALL POINT PEN (PRESS FIRMLY)

132445855 210
Sanchez, Roberto L.
10-01-1940

Dr. L. Hubbard

Date	Time	Treatment
1/14	10:50	Vancomycin 500 mg IV infusion over 6 hr
		②

PHYSICIAN'S ORDER WORKSHEET

Distribution:
(Original) Medical Record Copy
(Plies 3, 2, & 1) Pharmacy

T-5

1. Patient name: ______________________
2. Prescriber: ______________________
3. Drug name and strength: ______________________
4. Directions: ______________________

Medication Order #3

PHYSICIAN'S ORDER WORKSHEET

NOTE: ***Person initiating entry should write legibly, date the form using (Mo/Day/Yr.), enter time, sign, and indicate their title.***

USE BALL POINT PEN (PRESS FIRMLY)

82347665 835 A
George, Sarah M.
02-17-1961

Dr. L. Montgomery

Date	Time	Treatment
4/10	13:00	Ibuprofen 600 mg po q 6h
		②

PHYSICIAN'S ORDER WORKSHEET | Distribution: (Original) Medical Record Copy (Plies 3, 2, & 1) Pharmacy | **T-5**

1. Patient name: ______________________________
2. Prescriber: ______________________________
3. Drug name and strength: ______________________________
4. Directions: ______________________________

Medication Order #4

PHYSICIAN'S ORDER WORKSHEET

NOTE: ***Person initiating entry should write legibly, date the form using (Mo/Day/Yr.), enter time, sign, and indicate their title.***

USE BALL POINT PEN (PRESS FIRMLY)

782467199 1410 B
Smith, Cody M.
11-18-1975

Dr. L. Halberdier

Date	Time	Treatment
8/14	13:15	Ranitidine 150 mg infusion over 24 hr
		②

PHYSICIAN'S ORDER WORKSHEET | Distribution: (Original) Medical Record Copy (Plies 3, 2, & 1) Pharmacy | **T-5**

1. Patient name: ____
2. Prescriber: ____
3. Drug name and strength: ____
4. Directions: ____

LAB 7-1: Filling a Medication Order

Objective:

To follow the proper procedure for filling a medication order.

Pre-Lab Information:

Review Chapter 7, "Health-System Pharmacy," in your textbook.

Explanation:

The medication order form is a multipurpose tool for communication among various members of the healthcare team working within a health system. In addition to prescribed medications, this form can be used by the physician for ordering lab values, dietary considerations, X-rays, or other medical procedures, so it is imperative that pharmacy personnel be able to properly distinguish and interpret medication orders.

Hospitals can choose to use physical, hard-copy medication order forms. Alternatives are a physician order entry system (POE) or a computerized physician order entry system (CPOE), which is a computerized system in which orders are entered electronically into the hospital's networked system.

Activity:

Review each of the following medication orders, enter them into the pharmacy computer system to generate labels, fill the medications, and label the prescriptions for the pharmacist to review.

If you do not have access to a pharmacy computer system, you can use the blank label that appears at the end of this lab.

Medication Order #1

PHYSICIAN'S ORDER WORKSHEET

NOTE: ***Person initiating entry should write legibly, date the form using (Mo/Day/Yr.), enter time, sign, and indicate their title.***

USE BALL POINT PEN (PRESS FIRMLY)

63450091 105
Randall, Kristen F.
09-28-63

Dr. R. Manini

Date	Time	Treatment
3/30	10:30	Restoril 15mg po qhs prn sleep
		②

PHYSICIAN'S ORDER WORKSHEET

Distribution:
(Original) Medical Record Copy
(Plies 3, 2, & 1) Pharmacy

T-5

Medication Order # 2

PHYSICIAN'S ORDER WORKSHEET

NOTE: *Person initiating entry should write legibly, date the form using (Mo/Day/Yr.), enter time, sign, and indicate their title.*

USE BALL POINT PEN (PRESS FIRMLY)

51298556 620 B
Nguyen, Kim T.
05-05-1971

Dr. K. Tran

Date	Time	Treatment
9/8	8:30	VICODIN 5/500 PO PRN PAIN
		②

PHYSICIAN'S ORDER WORKSHEET

Distribution:
(Original) Medical Record Copy
(Plies 3, 2, & 1) Pharmacy

T-5

Medication Order #3

PHYSICIAN'S ORDER WORKSHEET

NOTE: ***Person initiating entry should write legibly, date the form using (Mo/Day/Yr.), enter time, sign, and indicate their title.***

USE BALL POINT PEN (PRESS FIRMLY)

93471287 515B
Goodman, Ronald B.
06-15-1958

Dr. K. Patel

Date	Time	Treatment
9/10	11:20	Diflucan 200 mg IV over 4 hrs

(2)

PHYSICIAN'S ORDER WORKSHEET

Distribution:
(Original) Medical Record Copy
(Plies 3, 2, & 1) Pharmacy

T-5

Use the following label template to perform this lab if you do not have access to a computer.

Hometown Pharmacy, 325 Main St., Shelbyville, TX 72349, phone 321-555-8765

Prescription #:

Patient:

Prescriber:

Prescription:

~~**Quantity:**~~

Directions:

Date Filled:

~~**Refills Remaining**~~**:**

Discussion Questions:

1. What was most the most challenging aspect of this lab for you?

2. Did you enter and fill each prescription accurately? If not, what mistakes did you make, and how can you avoid making such errors in the future?

Chapter 8
Technology in the Pharmacy

After completing Chapter 8 from the textbook, you should be able to:	Related Activity in the Workbook/Lab Manual
1. List the hardware and software components used in pharmacy computers and summarize their purpose.	Review Questions, PTCB Exam Practice Questions
2. Describe and discuss the use of automation and robotics in community pharmacies.	Review Questions, PTCB Exam Practice Questions
3. Describe and discuss the use of automation and robotics in health-system pharmacies.	Review Questions
4. Summarize the uses of personal digital assistants in medicine.	Review Questions, PTCB Exam Practice Questions
5. Define and explain telepharmacy practice.	Review Questions
6. Summarize the impact of patient confidentiality regulations on the use of technology in the pharmacy.	Review Questions

INTRODUCTION

Over the past few decades, technology has revolutionized the practice of pharmacy. Today, virtually every pharmacy uses computers, automated systems, and other technology platforms for its operations and management of pharmaceutical care. Technology is used in both community and health-system pharmacies. As a pharmacy technician, it is important for you to have a basic understanding of the different technologies that are available and being used in pharmacies. These include basic tools, such as computers, printers, modems, and scanners, as well as more advanced tools, such as automatic counters, dispensing systems, bar coding, and even robots. Although you will certainly learn a lot on the job, if you enter the workplace computer literate and familiar with some basic concepts, you will be comfortable managing technological changes as they arise.

REVIEW QUESTIONS

Match the following.

1. _____ hardware	a. connects computers via phone lines or cable
2. _____ hard drive	b. lists of information ordered in specific ways
3. _____ database	c. hardware that allows information to be entered
4. _____ CPU	d. primary software/program of a computer system
5. _____ applications	e. uses advanced telecommunications technology
6. _____ input devices	f. brain of the computer system
7. _____ keyboard	g. permanent memory for essential operations
8. _____ modem	h. mechanical and electrical components of a computer
9. _____ software	i. primary input device of a computer
10. _____ ROM	j. temporary memory used for inputting
11. _____ RAM	k. software/programs that perform specific functions
12. _____ operating system	l. main storage device
13. _____ PDA	m. programs and applications that control computers
14. _____ telepharmacy	n. portable electronic device that operates like a computer

True or False?

15. Electronic counters are a threat to pharmacy technician jobs.
    T F

16. The FDA mandates that all prescription medications contain a bar code.
    T F

17. A faxed prescription is considered a legal document in most states.
    T F

18. Patient profiling is a violation of federal discrimination laws.
    T F

19. A pharmacist can now utilize a PDA as a mobile reference center.
    T F

Fill in the blank.

20. Using telecommunications technology, pharmacists can provide care to patients in medically underserved areas at a distance. This is called _____________.

PHARMACY CALCULATION PROBLEMS

Calculate the following.

1. A patient's medical order reads: "cefazolin 1 gm IVPB q8hr × 3 days." How many grams of cefazolin will the patient receive in total?

2. A patient is receiving 1,500 mg of vancomycin IVPB daily in three divided doses. How many milligrams will the patient receive in each dose?

3. A technician runs a report and finds that an automated dispensing unit in the ER only has two vials of ondansetron left. The maximum par level for that medication is 20 vials. That item also has a minimum par set of five vials. How many vials should the technician restock?

4. A patient needs 25 mg hydroxyzine IV push. The vial contains 50 mg in each mL. How many milliliters will the patient need?

5. A patient is receiving 100 mL of normal saline IV every hour. How long will a 1,000 mL IV bag last?

PTCB EXAM PRACTICE QUESTIONS

1. What part of a computer is responsible for interpreting commands and running software applications?
   a. JAZ
   b. RAM
   c. CPU
   d. ROM

2. PDAs are used by many healthcare professionals, including pharmacists. In which setting are you most likely to find pharmacists using PDAs?
   a. chain drugstore
   b. independent community pharmacy
   c. health-system pharmacy
   d. mail-order pharmacy

3. Which of the following examples of pharmacy technology has not been associated with improved patient safety?
   a. computerized patient profiles
   b. automated dispensing systems
   c. central processing unit
   d. prescription filling robot

4. What information is contained in the bar code mandated by the FDA?
   a. NDC code
   b. DEA number
   c. Social Security number
   d. AWP

5. Which of the following is considered a hardware output device?
   a. keyboard
   b. mouse
   c. printer
   d. scanner

CHAPTER 9
Inventory Management and Health Insurance Billing

After completing Chapter 9 from the textbook, you should be able to:	Related Activity in the Workbook/Lab Manual
1. List and describe the various purchasing systems used in pharmacies.	Review Questions, PTCB Exam Practice Questions
2. List and describe the various methods of purchasing available to pharmacies.	Review Questions
3. Define and describe prescription formularies.	Review Questions
4. Describe and perform the steps necessary for placing orders.	Review Questions, PTCB Exam Practice Questions Activity 9-1, Activity 9-2
5. Describe and perform the steps necessary for receiving orders.	Review Questions, PTCB Exam Practice Questions Activity 9-2
6. Classify the reasons for product returns and describe the process of making returns.	Review Questions Activity 9-1
7. Describe and differentiate Medicare and Medicaid.	Review Questions, PTCB Exam Practice Questions
8. Recognize and define terms commonly used in insurance billing.	Review Questions, PTCB Exam Practice Questions
9. Describe and perform the steps in collecting data for insurance purposes.	Review Questions
10. Describe and perform the steps necessary to transmit a prescription for insurance.	Review Questions
11. List and explain common insurance billing errors and their solutions.	Review Questions

INTRODUCTION

Two of the most common duties you will perform as a pharmacy technician are inventory management and processing of third-party, or insurance, billing claims. Both tasks are vitally important to the pharmacy.

A pharmacy cannot dispense prescriptions if the proper medications are not in stock. A pharmacy obtains its inventory through a purchasing system, either as a member of a group purchasing system (GPO) or independently. The inventory is often based on an organization's formulary or the formularies approved by insurance carriers. A pharmacy's inventory must be closely and regularly monitored to ensure that adequate stock is available, to remove expired drugs, and to comply with any product recalls.

To operate effectively, the pharmacy must be reimbursed by insurance carriers in a timely fashion. Insurance billing requires a comprehensive knowledge of billing terms, codes, and policies, such as DAW codes, authorized days supply, and formularies. As a pharmacy technician, you can help prevent many insurance claim rejections by ensuring that all information is correctly entered into the pharmacy's computer system before a claim is submitted.

Although the management of inventory and health insurance billing varies by facility, as a pharmacy technician, you will be available to assist the pharmacist by handling these responsibilities and allowing the pharmacist to focus on more clinical aspects of pharmaceutical care provision.

REVIEW QUESTIONS

Fill in the blanks.

1. A request for reimbursement, from a healthcare provider to an insurance provider, for products or services rendered is known as a/an ______________.
2. The portion of the cost of a service or product that a patient pays out of pocket each time the service or product is provided is called the ______________.
3. ______________ is the notation used by prescribers to instruct the pharmacy to use the exact drug written (usually a brand-name drug).
4. ______________ is the number of days a dispensed quantity of medication will last.
5. A set amount that a client pays up front before insurance coverage applies is known as the ____________.
6. Drugs that have not been dispensed as of the manufacturer's printed expiration date are classified as ______________.
7. ______________ are listings of drugs approved for a specific purpose.
8. A ______________ is a collective purchasing system in which a pharmacy joins a GPO, which contracts with pharmaceutical manufacturers on behalf of its members.
9. A purchasing system in which the pharmacy is responsible for establishing contracts directly with each pharmaceutical manufacturer is a/an ______________.
10. A federally funded, state-administered insurance program for low-income and disadvantaged persons is ______________.
11. The federally funded and administered health insurance program is called ______________.
12. A company hired by the insurer to process claims is a/an ______________.
13. A procedure for obtaining medications, devices, and products for an organization is known as a/an ______________.
14. The process through which a drug manufacturer or the FDA requires that specific drugs be returned to the manufacturer because of a specific concern is known as a/an ______________.

Choose the best answer.

15. Formularies are used by:
    a. institutional pharmacies.
    b. insurance companies.
    c. ambulatory pharmacies.
    d. all of the above.

16. Inventory should be checked for "outdates":
    a. weekly.
    b. monthly.
    c. yearly.
    d. whenever there is time.

17. OTC products may be recalled by the:
    a. FDA.
    b. DEA.
    c. AFT.
    d. FTC.

18. A preferred provider organization (PPO) differs from a health maintenance organization (HMO) in that:
    a. patients have greater choice in selecting care providers in a PPO.
    b. HMOs are much larger organizations (such as Aetna) and serve more patients.
    c. both HMOs and PPOs are virtually identical in their operations.
    d. HMOs are operated by physicians and PPOs by insurance carriers.

Match the following.

19. _____ Class I Recall — **a.** someone has or could die from using a drug
20. _____ Class II Recall — **b.** a drug has been mislabeled or is noncompliant
21. _____ Class III Recall — **c.** a drug could cause harm, but is not deadly

PHARMACY CALCULATION PROBLEMS

Calculate the following.

1. The pharmacy's automated order system indicates that there are 240 hydrochlorothiazide 25 mg tablets left in inventory. If the system is programmed to reorder when the order point falls below 200, how many bottles of 100 tablets will the system order?

2. The pharmacy's automated order system indicates that there are 7 vials of Humulin R insulin left. How many vials will the system order if the reorder point falls below 10?

3. A small, independent pharmacy has a manual ordering system with maximum/minimum levels (in bottles) written on the shelf under the drug. If the maximum/minimum levels for nabumetone 500 mg are 4/2, and there is one bottle on the shelf, how many bottles should be reordered?

4. A customer is picking up three prescriptions and owes a co-pay of $7.50 on each one. If she hands the pharmacy clerk $30, how much change should the customer receive?

5. A pharmacy is running a special on cold medicines: buy two and get the third for 50% off. If a customer purchases three cold medicines that are all regularly $5.99 each, how much is the total cost to the customer?

PTCB EXAM PRACTICE QUESTIONS

1. A listing of the goods or items that a business will use in its normal operation is called a/an:
   a. purchasing.
   b. inventory.
   c. open formulary.
   d. closed formulary.

2. The goal of inventory management is:
   a. to ensure that drugs are available when they are needed.
   b. to maintain MSDS.
   c. to develop closed formularies.
   d. to increase use of wholesalers.

3. What do we call the minimum and maximum stock levels that are used to determine when to reorder a drug and how much to order?
   a. reorder points
   b. automatic ordering
   c. POS
   d. turnovers

4. What do we call the portion of the price of the medication that the patient is required to pay?
   a. co-insurance
   b. co-pay
   c. maximum allowable cost
   d. usual and customary price

5. Which of the following describes Medicaid?
   a. It is a federal/state program for the needy.
   b. It is a federal program for people over 65 years of age.
   c. It offers a completely open formulary.
   d. It is insurance for people with kidney failure.

ACTIVITY 9-1: Case Study — DEA Forms and Shipment Do Not Match

Instructions: Read the following scenario and then answer the critical thinking questions.

In your pharmacy, controlled medications are ordered by the vault technician. The process specifies that the vault technician fills out the DEA 222 forms and has the head pharmacist sign them. Upon arrival, two people check in the freight, matching up the shipment to the order. For many months, the two who have checked in the freight each time are the exact same pharmacist and pharmacy technician. This is acceptable because they are not the same persons who do the ordering.

One day, the pharmacy technician who checks in orders is absent and you are asked to help receive a shipment. You have the forms, and you and the pharmacist begin opening the totes. You work without incident until you get to the third tote and notice that the red locking tie is not sealed. You point it out to the pharmacist, who brushes it off, stating that it probably got caught on something. The pharmacist is also rushing you along because he has prescriptions to check. Continuing to match up the medications to the order form, you realize that you are short one #30-count bottle of Oxycontin® 10 mg. A recount brings about the same results.

You expect the pharmacist to be concerned, but he is not. He just keeps pushing you to "get on with it" and says that he will figure it out later. You are very uncomfortable with this direction; however, this is your head pharmacist giving the order.

1. What is the right thing to do here?

____

____

____

____

2. What are some possible explanations for the one missing bottle?

____

____

____

____

3. Can and should the ordering/checking-in process be altered to better prevent such situations?

____

____

____

____

4. Is there any reason why you should not do what the pharmacist directs you to do here?

____

____

____

____

ACTIVITY 9-2: Case Study — Out-of-Stock Item

Instructions: Read the following scenario and then answer the critical thinking questions.

It is late on a Saturday evening and the rural southwestern hospital where you work is the only medical facility open to the public. A middle-aged female comes into the emergency room after an assault, and the physician on duty prescribes a postexposure prophylaxis (PEP) starter pack. PEP is a course of anti-HIV drugs taken shortly after possible exposure to human immunodeficiency virus (HIV) infection; the pack includes a zidovudine (300 mg) and lamivudine (150 mg) combined tablet plus indinavir 400 mg taken over a specific time period. These medications, when taken shortly after HIV exposure, may help keep the patient from contracting HIV infection.

For some reason, either through poor supply or high demand, you discover that your pharmacy is completely out of indinavir in any dose. You are left with the task of obtaining some as soon as possible. There are only two independent pharmacies in the rural town where the hospital is located, and neither will be open on Sunday, leaving you unable to obtain a supply for at least two days. The nearest town is a two-and-a-half-hour drive away. What do you do?

1. What options do you have for obtaining the medication quickly?

____

____

____

____

2. Where do you think you can find this medication in the time allowed?

____

____

____

____

3. Detail how you would go about obtaining this medication, from time of contact to time of possession. How long does it realistically take?

____

____

____

____

CHAPTER 10
Introduction to Compounding

After completing Chapter 10 from the textbook, you should be able to:	Related Activity in the Workbook/Lab Manual
1. Explain the purpose and reason for compounding prescriptions.	Review Questions
2. Discuss the basic procedures involved in compounding.	Review Questions, PTCB Exam Practice Questions
3. List and describe the equipment, supplies, and facilities required for compounding.	Review Questions, PTCB Exam Practice Questions
4. List the major dosage forms used in compounding.	Review Questions, PTCB Exam Practice Questions
5. Discuss the considerations involved in flavoring a compounded prescription.	Review Questions, PTCB Exam Practice Questions

INTRODUCTION

Pharmaceutical *compounding* is the practice of extemporaneously preparing medications to meet the unique need of an individual patient according to the specific order of a physician or prescriber. Compounded medications may be either sterile or nonsterile and include suspensions, capsules, suppositories, topically applied medications, intravenous admixtures, and parenteral nutrition solutions.

Extemporaneous compounding is a special service provided by a number of community-based pharmacies. To assist the pharmacist in compounding medications, you will require additional training, skills, and practice. However, this unique area of pharmacy practice offers a number of advanced professional opportunities for those who pursue these skills.

REVIEW QUESTIONS

Match the following.

1. _____ comminuting
2. _____ compounding
3. _____ emulsion
4. _____ excipient
5. _____ geometric dilution
6. _____ suspension
7. _____ titration

a. contains nonsoluble ingredients
b. another word for titration
c. contains two unmixable liquids
d. substance added to make suitable consistency
e. reducing particle size by grinding
f. starts with smallest ingredient
g. extemporaneously preparing medication to meet needs of individual patients

Choose the best answer.

8. Which of the following is not a compounding resource?
   a. *United States Pharmacopoeia*
   b. Merck book of brand and generic drugs
   c. *Veterinary Drug Handbook*
   d. *Remington's Pharmaceutical Sciences*

9. Which of the following compounding steps should be completed before the others?
   a. Collect all necessary ingredients.
   b. Write up a compounding worksheet.
   c. Weigh each ingredient.
   d. Follow the formula.

10. Which of the following is more appropriate for melting bases?
    a. magnetic stir plate
    b. heat gun
    c. hotplate
    d. electronic mortar and pestle

11. When using geometric dilution, one should start with the:
    a. ingredient needed in the smallest amount.
    b. ingredient needed in the largest amount.
    c. equal amounts of each ingredient.
    d. the liquid or binding base.

12. Assuming that only the following dosage forms were suitable, which is the desirable choice for animal patients?
    a. cream
    b. ointment
    c. transdermal gel
    d. injection

Match the following.

13. _____ capsule
14. _____ emulsion
15. _____ stick
16. _____ troche
17. _____ cream
18. _____ suspension
19. _____ paste
20. _____ ointment

a. topical application of anesthetics or antivirals
b. dissipates into the skin when applied
c. liquid preparation that contains insolubles
d. oral dosage form used for more than 100 years
e. oral form that disintegrates over time
f. liquid/semisolid form that can be taken orally or applied topically
g. stiff, viscous ointment
h. semisolid preparation that stays on top of skin

True or False?

21. Otic preparations may be used ophthalmically.

    T F

22. The most common form of compounded transdermal gel therapy is a two-phase vehicle made from pluronic lecithin organogel.

    T F

23. Using the proper coloring and flavoring in medications is important for patient compliance.

    T F

24. One of the five basic flavoring techniques is physiological.

    T F

25. Aseptic, or sterile, technique should be used in all compounding.

    T F

PHARMACY CALCULATION PROBLEMS

Calculate the following.

1. Tom is compounding a prescription that calls for 15 g betamethasone 0.05% cream, 15 g diphenhydramine cream, then qsad 60 g with aquaphilic ointment. How much aquaphilic ointment will he need to add to this compound?

2. A prescription was brought to the pharmacy for a product that is not commercially available. It calls for clindamycin 4,500 mg qsad 120 mL with lubricating lotion. If the clindamycin is available in 300 mg capsules, how many capsules should be opened for use in this compound?

3. How many sucralfate 1 g tablets will you need for an oral suspension that calls for 20 g sucralfate as the active ingredient?

4. A pharmacy received a faxed order from a veterinarian for celecoxib 25 mg chicken dog treats, #100. If the celecoxib comes in 100 mg capsules, how many capsules should be mixed in the chicken base to make 100 treats?

5. A special compound requires equal parts zinc oxide 20% ointment, nystatin ointment, and hydrocortisone 0.5% ointment. If the prescription calls for 60 grams, how many grams of each ointment will be needed?

PTCB EXAM PRACTICE QUESTIONS

1. A two-phase system consisting of a finely divided solid dispersed in a liquid is a/an:
   a. suspension.
   b. emulsion.
   c. solution.
   d. trituration.

2. What is the on-demand preparation of a drug product according to a physician's prescription?
   a. IVPB
   b. extemporaneous compounding
   c. trituration
   d. spatulation

3. The fine grinding of a powder is called:
   a. extemporaneous compounding.
   b. suspension.
   c. emulsion.
   d. trituration.

4. Clear liquids in which the drug is completely dissolved are called:
   a. sublimations.
   b. suspensions.
   c. solutions.
   d. emulsions.

5. A system containing two immiscible liquids with one dispersed in the other is called a/an:
   a. emulsion.
   b. suspension.
   c. syrup.
   d. solution.

ACTIVITY 10-1: Case Study—Childproof Containers

Instructions: Read the following scenario and then answer the critical thinking questions.

Mrs. Gaynor has been on estrogen therapy for a short time now and is beginning to feel much better. Her premenopausal hot flashes and night sweats have subsided. She receives an 8 oz. jar of a custom-compounded estrogen cream made specifically for her. She uses it daily and keeps the jar under a sink in the bathroom.

While her prepubescent grandson is visiting, he becomes curious and applies some of the cream. He thinks it must be something special because of the claims made on the jar about feeling much better. The grandson continues to do this, without anyone's knowledge, as he visits on a weekly basis. Meanwhile, Mrs. Gaynor is receiving more frequent refills through the compounding pharmacy.

Soon the grandson develops gynecomastia (the development of abnormally large mammary glands that can sometimes secrete milk). A doctor's visit confirms that the grandson has been exposed to large amounts of estrogen and enlists the family's help in finding the source.

1. What steps could the compounding pharmacy take to help prevent this situation?

2. What steps could the grandmother take to help prevent easy access by the grandson?

3. From the information provided, what signs or "flags" were present to indicate that there might be a problem?

CHAPTER 11

Introduction to Sterile Products

After completing Chapter 11 from the textbook, you should be able to:	Related Activity in the Workbook/Lab Manual
1. List the equipment and supplies used in preparing sterile products.	Review Questions, PTCB Exam Practice Questions Activity 11-1, Lab 11-1, Lab 11-2
2. List the routes of administration associated with sterile products.	Review Questions, PTCB Exam Practice Questions Activity 11-1, Lab 11-1, Lab 11-2
3. Discuss special concerns regarding chemotherapy and cytotoxic drugs.	Review Questions, PTCB Exam Practice Questions

INTRODUCTION

Sterile compounding is the preparation of compounded medications using aseptic technique, or the process of performing a procedure under controlled conditions in a manner that minimizes the chance of contamination of the preparation. Following proper aseptic techniques ensures that all compounded products remain free of bacteria, fungi, pyrogens, infectives, and other microorganisms. To ensure sterility, these products are prepared in laminar flow hoods, including horizontal flow hoods and biological safety cabinets, which contain a high-efficiency particulate air (HEPA) filter.

Patients generally receive sterile products parenterally through various administration sites, such as veins (IV) and muscle tissue (IM). Other sterile products include total parenteral nutrition (TPNs), as well as ophthalmic and otic preparations.

Sterile product preparation can be a complex, high-risk process in the healthcare setting. As a pharmacy technician with proper training, you can play an integral role in the procurement, storage, preparation, and distribution of sterile products.

REVIEW QUESTIONS

Match the following.

1. _____ antineoplastics	**a.** a larger volume of solution given at a steady rate
2. _____ intradermal	**b.** injection into a muscle
3. _____ infusion	**c.** the same tonicity as red blood cells
4. _____ pH	**d.** injection into the spine
5. _____ buffer capacity	**e.** medications to treat cancer
6. _____ intramuscular	**f.** injection into the skin
7. _____ isotonicity	**g.** solid that forms in a solution
8. _____ precipitate	**h.** ability of a solution to resist a change in pH
9. _____ intrathecal	**i.** the degree of acidity

Choose the best answer.

10. A bevel is:
   a. an angle cut to measure cc/mL.
   b. a rounded-edge needle.
   c. the sharp pointed end of a needle.
   d. the only part of a needle that can be touched.

11. Medication used to treat cancer is called:
   a. antitoxin.
   b. chemotherapy.
   c. radiation.
   d. cytoblast.

12. Class 100 environment is:
   a. a classification of airflow units.
   b. a dimensional measurement of the floor plan.
   c. an airflow of 100 psi.
   d. the best level of sterility available.

13. HEPA refers to:
   a. patient privacy rights.
   b. a large insurance group.
   c. a type of air filter.
   d. the government group that inspects air filters.

Identify and indicate the parts of a needle.

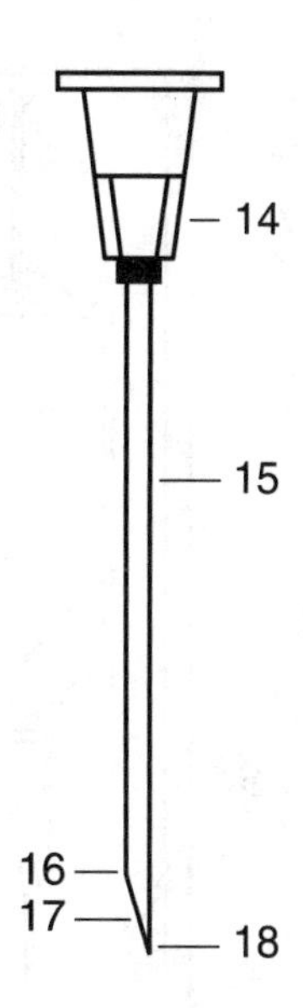

14. ______________
15. ______________
16. ______________
17. ______________
18. ______________

Identify and indicate the parts of a syringe.

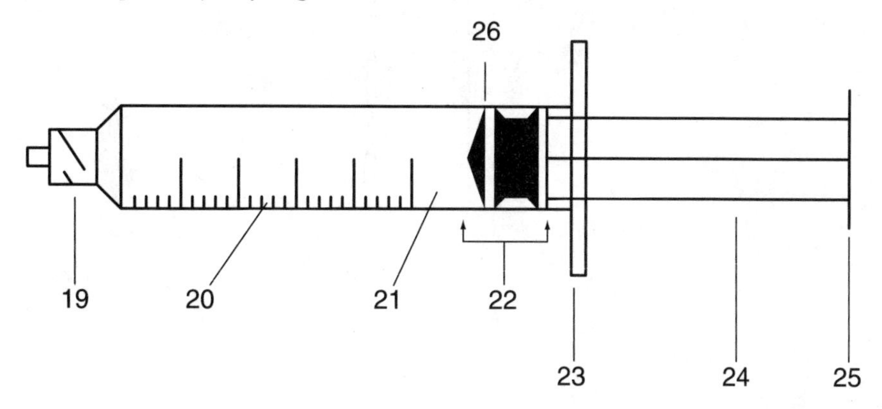

19. ______________
20. ______________
21. ______________
22. ______________
23. ______________
24. ______________
25. ______________
26. ______________

Identify and indicate the parts of an IV bag system.

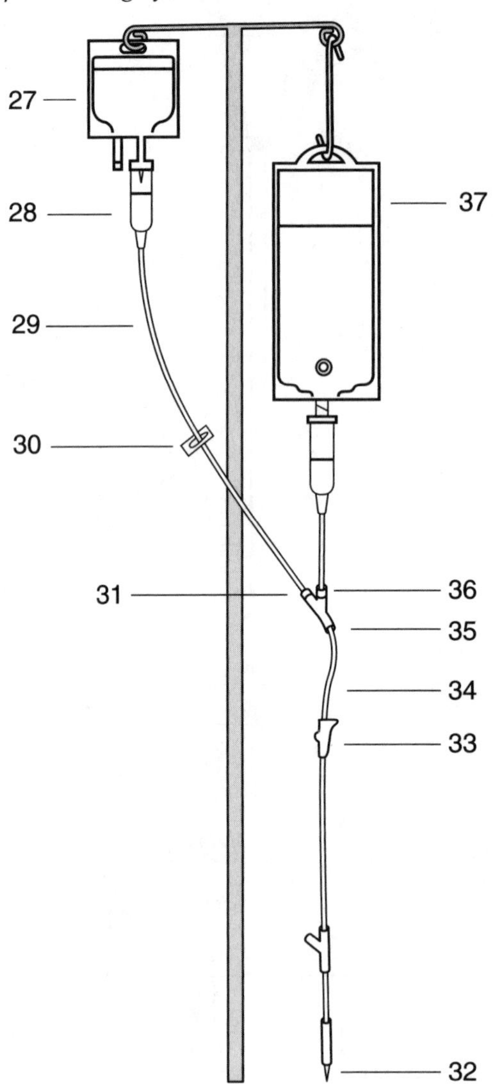

27. ____________

28. ____________

29. ____________

30. ____________

31. ____________

32. ____________

33. ____________

34. ____________

35. ____________

36. ____________

37. ____________

PHARMACY CALCULATION PROBLEMS

Calculate the following.

1. A medical order states that a patient is to receive 500 mL of 0.9% sodium chloride IV over 2 hours. How fast is the IV running in mL/hr?

2. A technician prepares a sterile compound that contains 100 mg/mL of active drug. How many mL are required for a dose of 800 mg?

3. If a bulk bottle of IV multivitamins contains 50 mL, how many 10 mL doses can be obtained from the bottle?

4. After reconstitution, ceftriaxone for IM injection contains 350 mg/mL. How many milligrams are in 2.5 milliliters?

5. A 1,000 mL bag of 5% dextrose with 20 mEq KCl is infusing at 125 mL/hr. How many hours will the bag last before it must be replaced?

PTCB EXAM PRACTICE QUESTIONS

1. When using a horizontal laminar airflow hood, how far should the technician work inside the hood?
   a. at least two inches
   b. at least four inches
   c. at least six inches
   d. at least eight inches

2. In a laminar airflow hood, the air flows in how many direction(s)?
   a. four
   b. three
   c. two
   d. one

3. In horizontal laminar airflow hoods, the air blows in which direction?
   a. down toward the work area
   b. away from the operator
   c. toward the operator
   d. up toward the HEPA filter

4. Large-volume parenterals (LVPs) usually have what kind of infusion rates?
   a. intermittent
   b. rapid
   c. slow
   d. instantaneous

5. Vertical airflow hoods have what characteristic?
   a. vertical airflow down toward the product
   b. horizontal airflow away from the operator
   c. vertical airflow up toward the HEPA filter
   d. horizontal airflow toward the operator

ACTIVITY 11-1: Case Study—Identifying Errors in Aseptic Technique

Read the following scenario and identify at least 10 aseptic errors that the pharmacy technician made. Describe ways to improve her technique.

As a student, you are assigned to observe the aseptic technique of the IV room technician. Mindy is scheduled to work in the IV room this morning, but she stayed up too late the night before and had to rush to get to work on time. Before leaving home, she quickly put on some makeup to cover up the circles under her eyes. After punching in late, she began by washing her hands for 10 seconds, missing the dirt she had under her fingernails. After drying her hands with a paper towel, she threw the towel away and then shut off the faucet with her right hand. Next, she put on her gloves, a face mask, and a gown.

Once gowned, Mindy began cleaning the laminar airflow hood with blue window cleaner, using paper towels. She randomly wiped down the hood in circular patterns, and then began preparations for compounding some IV orders. She piled several syringes and needles in the hood, as well as several vials of various medications for the prescriptions that had to be prepared.

At this point, Mindy told you she needed a cup of coffee to perk herself up, so she excused herself to grab some coffee in the break area. A few minutes later, she returned to the clean room with the coffee. She resumed preparing the IVs, selecting several small-volume bags that she would need for the medications. She put those in the hood next to the syringes and began removing the caps to the vials. She assembled a needle and syringe, pulled out the appropriate volume from one of the vials, and immediately injected it into a small-volume bag. It was at this point that you recognized she would need more aseptic training.

Critical Thinking Questions:

1. List at least 10 aseptic errors made in this scenario, then describe the correct solutions to the errors.

   Mistake 1: ______________________________

   Correct Procedure: ______________________________

   ____

   ____

   ____

   Mistake 2: ______________________________

   Correct Procedure: ______________________________

   ____

   ____

   ____

Mistake 3: ______________________________

Correct Procedure: ______________________________

____

____

____

Mistake 4: ______________________________

Correct Procedure: ______________________________

____

____

____

Mistake 5: ______________________________

Correct Procedure: ______________________________

____

____

____

Mistake 6: ______________________________

Correct Procedure: ______________________________

____

____

____

Mistake 7: ______________________________

Correct Procedure: ______________________________

____

____

____

Mistake 8: ______________________________

Correct Procedure: ______________________________

____

____

____

Mistake 9: ______________________________

Correct Procedure: ______________________________

____

____

____

Mistake 10: ___

Correct Procedure: ___

___

___

___

2. How could this pharmacy technician's negligent technique result in serious harm to a patient?

___

___

___

___

___

LAB 11-1: Withdrawing Medication from a Vial or Glass Ampule

Objective:

Demonstrate the techniques involved in withdrawing medications from vials or ampules.

Pre-Lab Information:

- Review Chapter 11 in your textbook for review of aseptic compounding, needles, and syringes.
- Gather the following materials:
  - sterile vials and ampules of 0.9% sodium chloride
  - 10 mL syringes
  - 18 gauge, 1-1/2 inch needles
  - filter needles
  - gloves
  - alcohol swabs

Explanation:

You will learn the proper aseptic techniques for withdrawing medication from vials and ampules. If your instructor is unable to provide a lab component, your local hospital pharmacy may provide a demonstration for students upon request.

Activity:

Your instructor will take you through the proper procedures for withdrawing medication from vials and glass ampules. You will then have the opportunity to practice some of these techniques in class. If a laminar airflow hood is not available, you will need to use a little imagination regarding true aseptic technique.

Key points for working with vials:

1. Always observe the six-inch rule and critical areas when working with sterile products in a laminar airflow hood.
2. Always disinfect the top of the vial with an alcohol swab. One single swipe in one direction should be adequate to disinfect the vial and its stopper. Wait a moment for the alcohol to evaporate before entering the vial with a needle.
3. Attach a needle to a syringe of appropriate size. Before entering the vial, always draw some air into the syringe, to a volume that is slightly less than you want to withdraw from the vial. This extra air will be pushed into the vial before withdrawing the contents to help equalize the air pressure and make the withdrawal easier to accomplish.
4. Use care entering the vial with the needle. Using too large a needle or the wrong entry technique could result in "coring" of the stopper, which could leave fragments of the stopper in the medication. Adding too much air to the vial could also cause some of the medication to accidentally spray out, reducing the volume available for use and contaminating the hood.
5. With the bevel facing up, press the needle into the middle of the stopper until it has completely broken the seal. Be careful not to interrupt any of the airflow between the hood and the entry point shared between the vial and the needle. This process can be challenging for the beginner. Carefully tip the vial upside down, maintaining aseptic technique, and gently push some of the air from the syringe into the vial. The syringe will usually start to withdraw some of the fluid on its own. Repeat the process until all the air is out of the syringe and you have withdrawn the correct amount of fluid.
6. The syringe is now ready either to be capped or to be added to an IV bag for further dilution.

Key points for working with ampules:

1. Always observe the six-inch rule and critical areas when working with sterile products in a laminar airflow hood.
2. Always disinfect the narrow portion of the ampule with an alcohol swab.
3. Make sure that no liquid is trapped in the neck of the ampule. Tapping the ampule gently with a finger usually releases any liquid from the neck, allowing it to settle in the bottom.
4. Break the ampule open at the weakest part around the neck, usually indicated by a dot or a stripe. Be sure to break it open toward the side of the hood and not into the back of the hood. Glass fragments can damage the HEPA filter, which is located behind the grate at the back of the hood.
5. When withdrawing medication from a glass ampule, you must use a filter needle in order to filter out any glass particles that may have gotten into the medication. You do not need to withdraw air into the syringe before withdrawing medication from an ampule, because there is no longer a vacuum once you have broken open the ampule.
6. Using a filter needle attached to an appropriate syringe, tilt the ampule slightly in order to withdraw the amount of medication desired. You may need to adjust the volume in the syringe and repeat until you have the correct amount.
7. If the contents of the syringe are to be added to an IV bag, you must first change to a new, nonfiltered needle. If you keep the same needle, all of the glass particles you trapped will be pushed into the IV bag along with the medication, negating the whole filtering process.
8. Alternatively, some technicians prefer to draw the medication from the ampule with a regular needle, and then change to a filter needle before injecting the medication into an IV bag. Either method prevents glass particles from getting into the IV.

Questions:

1. Why do you need to pull air into the syringe before withdrawing medication from a vial?

____

____

____

2. Why do you need to swab off the top of a vial or an ampule with alcohol?

____

____

____

3. Why is it important to use a filter needle when working with glass ampules?

____

____

____

4. Why should you break open an ampule toward the side of the hood instead of toward the back of the hood?

____

____

____

5. Why do you not need to pull air into the syringe before withdrawing medication from an ampule?

____

____

____

LAB 11-2: Transferring Liquid into an IV Bag

Objective:

Understand the technique involved in transferring liquid medication from a syringe into an IV bag so that you are able to apply the technique in a pharmacy setting.

Pre-Lab Information:

Review Chapter 11 in your textbook for information regarding aseptic technique and IV medications.

Explanation:

Many IV medications have to be further diluted before they are administered to patients. This process, also known as *sterile compounding,* is most often done with one or more syringes and an IV bag containing an isotonic fluid. In this activity, you will learn the proper aseptic technique for transferring solutions from a syringe into the IV bag, identify which port on the IV bag is used for the transfer, and learn how to add multiple products to the same bag.

Activity:

When compounding sterile products, follow these simple guidelines:

1. Read the prescription label to determine which products you need to use.
2. Select the correct IV bag and size (example: dextrose 5%, 100 mL) and the correct medication that will be transferred to this bag (example: diltiazem 125 mg/25 mL).
3. Remove the outer packaging and wipe down the entire bag with alcohol (in a clean room, parts of these processes may be done by a co-worker).
4. Place the disinfected bag on a hanger in the laminar airflow hood.
5. Strip off the seal to the center port of the IV bag and disinfect the port with an alcohol swab. (The port is usually in the middle with a blue seal, but certain IV bags have more than one port for pharmacy use.)
6. Prepare the medication for transfer to the IV bag. If it comes in a sterile powder, first follow the directions for reconstitution; then draw the appropriate amount of medication into a syringe, using aseptic technique.
7. Taking care to observe the critical areas of the hood and the six-inch rule, insert the needle (which is still attached to the syringe of medication from step 6) straight into the center of the port. You will need to pass the needle through the outer core and through an inner membrane. Try to keep the needle straight so as not to puncture the side of the port or the bag. A puncture will void the sterility of all the products involved and you will have to start over with new supplies.
8. Once the needle has passed the inner membrane, gently push the fluid from the syringe into the bag; then carefully pull out the needle and the syringe.
9. If your pharmacist has not double-checked your work at this point, some pharmacies allow you to pull the empty syringe back with air to the volume that you placed in the bag, to indicate how much drug you used.
10. After your work has been checked by a pharmacist, place a cap or seal over the port you just used (this step may be omitted depending on the pharmacy). Remove the IV from the hook, gently shake the bag to distribute the drug, and then label the bag appropriately.
11. If multiple drugs are used in the same bag, gently shake the IV bag between medications to avoid possible precipitation. "Banana bags," which got their nickname from their yellow color, are a multivitamin/mineral infusion and are a good example of a prescription for which you would use more than one drug in a bag.

These step-by-step instructions can be used to prepare most sterile products that require further dilution in an IV bag. You or your instructor may be able to get permission from a local hospital to demonstrate these techniques or allow you to practice.

Questions:

1. What might happen if a punctured bag accidentally made it out of the pharmacy and were hung for a patient?

____

____

____

____

2. What might happen if you added several products to an IV bag without mixing in between additions?

____

____

____

____

3. Why is it so important to practice aseptic technique when preparing IV medications?

____

____

____

____

4. While you are performing a fluid transfer, you accidently lose your grip on the syringe and it falls onto the hood. You discover that the needle has touched the surface of the hood. What should you do?

____

____

____

____

Chapter 12
Basic Math Skills

After completing Chapter 12 from the textbook, you should be able to:	Related Activity in the Workbook/Lab Manual
1. Determine the value of a decimal.	Review Questions Pharmacy Calculation Problems PTCB Exam Practice Questions
2. Add, subtract, multiply, and divide decimals.	Review Questions Pharmacy Calculation Problems PTCB Exam Practice Questions Activity 12-1
3. Recognize and interpret Roman numerals.	Review Questions Pharmacy Calculation Problems PTCB Exam Practice Questions
4. Change Roman numerals to Arabic numerals.	Review Questions Pharmacy Calculation Problems PTCB Exam Practice Questions
5. Change Arabic numerals to Roman numerals.	Review Questions Pharmacy Calculation Problems PTCB Exam Practice Questions
6. Describe the different types of common fractions.	Review Questions Activity 12-4
7. Add, subtract, multiply, and divide fractions.	Review Questions Pharmacy Calculation Problems PTCB Exam Practice Questions Activity 12-2
8. Define a ratio.	Review Questions Activity 12-4
9. Define a proportion.	Review Questions Activity 12-4
10. Solve math problems by using ratios and proportions.	Review Questions Pharmacy Calculation Problems PTCB Exam Practice Questions Activity 12-3

INTRODUCTION

Knowledge of basic arithmetic is essential for today's pharmacy technician. You need basic math skills to understand and perform drug preparations. Nearly every aspect of drug dispensing requires a consideration of numbers. All advanced pharmacy calculations, which are explained throughout this text, rely on a solid understanding of basic math principles. Remember that Chapter 12 in your textbook is designed to serve as a review of these general principles and as an assessment of your basic math skills; the activities in this workbook/lab manual will provide you with additional review.

REVIEW QUESTIONS

Match the following.

1. _____ common fractions
2. _____ complex fractions
3. _____ cross-multiplication
4. _____ decimal fractions
5. _____ denominator
6. _____ fraction line
7. _____ improper fraction
8. _____ numerator
9. _____ proper fraction
10. _____ proportion
11. _____ ratio
12. _____ Roman numerals
13. _____ simple fractions

a. bottom value of a fraction; placed beneath the fraction line

b. setting up two ratios or fractions in relationship to each other as a proportion and solving for the unknown variable

c. symbol representing the division of two values; placed between the numerator and denominator of a fraction

d. fractions written with a numerator separated by a fraction line from and positioned above a denominator

e. fraction in which both the numerator and the denominator are themselves common fractions

f. fractions written as a whole number with a zero and a decimal point in front of the value

g. a fraction in which the value of the numerator is smaller than the value of the denominator

h. letters and symbols used to represent numbers

i. the top value of a fraction; placed above the fraction line

j. the expression of a relationship of two numbers, written with a colon (:) between the numbers

k. proper fraction, with both the numerator and denominator reduced to lowest terms

l. fraction in which the value of the numerator is larger than the value of the denominator

m. two or more equivalent ratios or fractions that both represent the same value

Choose the best answer.

14. Which of these decimals has the highest value?

a. 0.21
b. 0.35
c. 0.31
d. 0.42

15. Which of these decimals has the highest value?

a. 1.37
b. 1.43
c. 1.89
d. 1.25

16. Which of these decimals has the lowest value?
   a. 12.4
   b. 12.006
   c. 12.03
   d. 12.891

17. Which of these decimals has the lowest value?
   a. 0.15
   b. 0.16
   c. 0.016
   d. 0.22

Multiply the following decimals.

18. $8.6 \times 0.24 =$ ____________
19. $6.58 \times 2.26 =$ ____________
20. $5.5 \times 4.986 =$ ____________

Divide the following decimals.

21. $0.98 \div 0.3 =$ ____________
22. $5.5 \div 0.4 =$ ____________
23. $6.0 \div 0.66 =$ ____________

Change these Roman numerals to Arabic.

24. XXVII ____________
25. MDLXVI ____________
26. XC ____________
27. CL ____________
28. XXI ____________
29. LX ____________
30. CCCLXV ____________

PHARMACY CALCULATION PROBLEMS

Calculate the following.

1. Add the following fractions: $\frac{2}{4} + \frac{1}{8} + \frac{3}{16} =$

2. Solve for X: $\frac{50}{2} = \frac{30}{X}$

3. Solve for X: 250 mg/1 mL $= \frac{X}{5}$ mL

4. Solve for X: 1,000 mcg/1 mL = $\frac{X}{2.5}$ mL

5. A physician writes a prescription for CXX tablets. If the patient takes 11 tablets qid, how many days will the supply last?

PTCB EXAM PRACTICE QUESTIONS

1. How many capsules will be taken in three days if a prescription order reads tetracycline 250 mg/capsule, one capsule qid?
   a. 16
   b. 12
   c. 3
   d. 6

2. How would you express 33.3% as a decimal?
   a. 33.3
   b. 0.333
   c. 3.33
   d. 333

3. What is 20% of 30?
   a. 6
   b. 60
   c. 3
   d. 300

4. How would you express 49 as a Roman numeral?
   a. IL
   b. XLVIIII
   c. XXXXVIIII
   d. XLIX

5. How would you round 145.1155 to the nearest hundredth?
   a. 145.1
   b. 145.11
   c. 145.12
   d. 145.116

ACTIVITY 12-1: Case Study—How Much?

Instructions: Read the following scenario and then answer the critical thinking questions.

Ms. Kipsky is an older woman who is on a very tight budget. She has worked at the local fabric store part time since her children all moved out of the house. In addition to this part-time job she receives an overdue child support check every now and then that helps her make it to the next payday. Luckily, she does not have any health conditions that require her to be on medicine and she is very glad about that; she just would not be able to afford it on top of her bills and bus fare to get to work every day.

It is deep into winter in the small town Ms. Kipsky works in when she comes to the independent pharmacy where you work, bearing a prescription for a mild bacterial infection. She tried to beat this infection for about a week and finally she went to the free clinic, where they prescribed amoxicillin suspension 250 mg/5 mL, 2 teaspoonfuls every 8 hours until gone (times 10 days).

Unfortunately for Ms. Kipsky, payday is not until next Friday and today is only Saturday. She brings the prescription to the pharmacy to be filled and asks the cost. You calculate the amount for her as $30.

1. Ms. Kipsky is uninsured and is paying cash. She asks you how much of the medication she will get if she can only pay for half right now.

2. Ms. Kipsky checks her purse and finds that she has only $5.00. She wants to know how much medicine that will buy. (Use the formula based on $30 for the entire prescription amount.)

3. She next asks how many doses she could get for $10.

ACTIVITY 12-2: Case Study—A Tapering Dose

Instructions: Read the following scenario and then answer the critical thinking questions.

Mr. Mindes is a regular customer at your retail pharmacy. His medication profile seems to be a who's-who of allergy medicines. Your pharmacy typically begins to see Mr. Mindes in early spring when the rain slows down and the flowers start to bloom. He has tried a variety of medications to help relieve allergy symptoms, such as fexofenadine, chlorpheniramine, and loratadine. He also has a nasal spray that keeps his sinuses clear during allergy attacks.

In spite of Mr. Mindes's preparation for each spring's natural bounties, this year he finds that he has actually acquired an infection that makes it tough for him to breathe. He has an uncomfortable case of bronchitis. His provider is prescribing a course of prednisone to help reduce the inflammation in his lungs.

The prescription is as follows: 5 tablets daily for 5 days, then 4 tablets daily for 5 days, then 3 tablets daily for 5 days, then 2 tablets daily for 5 days, then 1 tablet daily for 6 days.

1. What is the total number of tablets needed to fill the complete prescription?

2. At exactly halfway through his course of prednisone treatment, how many tablets will Mr. Mindes have left in the bottle?

3. With three days to the end of his treatment and last dose, how many tablets are left in his prescription bottle?

____

____

ACTIVITY 12-3: Case Study—Cream Compound

Instructions: Read the following scenario and then answer the critical thinking questions.

Sebastian, a very nice old man, has a very not-nice skin condition. He always has some rash or major itching problem that just will not go away. Over the years he has tried it all: a multitude of moisturizers, none of which seem to keep his skin from getting all these bumps that make him itch constantly.

Sebastian put up with this after the doctors told him it was not a medical condition like psoriasis or eczema. He has tried a variety of home remedies and herbal concoctions to make it go away, but it persists. Once in a while it will move around, but basically the active area remains on his lower left and right arms near the elbows.

One day Sebastian is with his doctor and the rash is just a little bit worse. The doctor decides to try a compound of two ingredients that he thinks might help alleviate the itching and add more moisture to the skin. Sebastian brings the prescription to your pharmacy to have it filled. The prescription is for 60% of ingredient A and 40% of ingredient B. The total amount is 155 grams.

1. How many grams of each of the ingredients will be used to make the compound?

____

____

____

____

2. If Sebastian wants to pick up only 80% of his prescription today, how many grams is he going to get?

____

____

3. Sebastian has 3.5 refills on his prescription. He is going out of town for 3 months and would like to pick up the entire amount today. How many grams is he going to get with all the refills?

____

____

ACTIVITY 12-4: Math Definitions

Match the math term in the left-hand column with its definition in the right-hand column.

Term

1. _____ proportion
2. _____ common fraction
3. _____ improper fraction
4. _____ simple fraction
5. _____ proper fraction
6. _____ ratio

Definition

a. can be expressed as one number that is set on a fraction line above another number
b. the value of the numerator is smaller than the value of the denominator
c. expresses the relationship of two numbers
d. two or more equivalent ratios or fractions that both represent the same value
e. the value of the numerator is larger than the value of the denominator
f. cannot be reduced to any lower terms

CHAPTER 13
Measurement Systems

After completing Chapter 13 from the textbook, you should be able to:	Related Activity in the Workbook/Lab Manual
1. List the three fundamental systems of measurement.	Review Questions Pharmacy Calculation Problems PTCB Exam Practice Questions
2. List the three primary units of the metric system.	Review Questions Pharmacy Calculation Problems PTCB Exam Practice Questions
3. Define the various prefixes used in the metric system.	Review Questions Pharmacy Calculation Problems PTCB Exam Practice Questions
4. Recognize abbreviations used in measurements.	Review Questions Pharmacy Calculation Problems PTCB Exam Practice Questions Activity 13-1, Activity 13-2, Activity 13-3
5. Explain the use of International Units and milliequivalents.	Review Questions Pharmacy Calculation Problems PTCB Exam Practice Questions
6. Convert measurements between the household system and the metric system.	Review Questions Pharmacy Calculation Problems PTCB Exam Practice Questions
7. Convert measurements between the apothecary system and the metric system.	Review Questions Pharmacy Calculation Problems PTCB Exam Practice Questions
8. Perform temperature conversions.	Review Questions Pharmacy Calculation Problems PTCB Exam Practice Questions Activity 13-3

INTRODUCTION

Three fundamental systems of measurement are used to calculate dosages: the metric, apothecary, and household systems. Most prescriptions are written using the metric system. Regardless of your practice setting as a pharmacy technician, you must understand each system and how to convert from one system to another. With practice, the conversions you need to calculate dosages will become second nature to you. Until that time, use the charts and formulas from Chapter 13 as a guide. Remember that although miscalculating a conversion may seem to be a minor issue, it could have irrevocable effects on a patient's health.

REVIEW QUESTIONS

Match the following.

1. _____ apothecary system	a. measurement of a drug in terms of its action
2. _____ avoirdupois system	b. unit of length in the metric system
3. _____ household system	c. based on the number of grams in 1 milliliter
4. _____ International Units	d. metric unit of volume
5. _____ metric system	e. international temperature unit
6. _____ Celsius	f. metric unit of weight
7. _____ Fahrenheit	g. international and scientific system of measurement
8. _____ grain	h. common system of measurement in the United States
9. _____ milliequivalent	i. Old English system of weight measurement
10. _____ gram	j. American measurement of temperature
11. _____ liter	k. American measurement for weight
12. _____ meter	l. primary unit of the apothecary system

Choose the best answer.

13. If you are denoting 2 tenths of a milligram, you would write:
    a. 2/10 mg
    b. 0.2 mg
    c. 2 mg
    d. .2 mg

14. 2 g is equivalent to:
    a. 2,000 mg
    b. 20,000 mg
    c. 200 mg
    d. 20 mg

15. 8 ounces is equivalent to how many mL?
    a. 16
    b. 24
    c. 240
    d. 160

16. There are 16 ounces in a pint. How many milliliters is that?
    a. 480
    b. 48
    c. 4.8
    d. 4,800

17. If Mary is to take 2 teaspoonfuls bid for 10 days, how many mL should be dispensed?
    a. 20,000
    b. 2,000
    c. 200
    d. 20

Match the following.

18. _____ micro
19. _____ kilo
20. _____ milli
21. _____ centi

a. one-hundredth of the base
b. one thousand of the base
c. one-millionth of the base
d. one-thousandth of the base

PHARMACY CALCULATION PROBLEMS

Calculate the following.

1. According to the prescription, a patient uses latanoprost ophthalmic drops "1 gtts os qd." If the bottle only comes in 2.5 mL, how many days will the supply last?

2. Metronidazole IV comes in a 500 mg/100 mL concentration. If the patient received 100 mL × 8 doses, how many grams of metronidazole were given in total?

3. A prescription calls for 8 fl. oz. of guaifenesin a.c. syrup. If the patient is to take 5 mL po qid, how long will the bottle last?

4. A patient is to take 1 g valacyclovir po bid × 5 days. If the medication comes in 500 mg tablets, how many tablets will the patient need?

5. A TPN contains 2.25 L and is running at 120 mL/hr. How many hours will the TPN last?

PTCB EXAM PRACTICE QUESTIONS

1. A prescription is written for hydrocortisone 5% in zinc oxide—dispense 50 g. How many hydrocortisone 50 mg tablets are needed to prepare this compound?
   a. 2,500
   b. 2.5
   c. 5
   d. 50

2. Potassium chloride 30 mEq is to be given in 1,000 mL of IV fluid. Available vials contain 40 mEq/20 mL. How many mL of the drug would you use?
   a. 1.5
   b. 15
   c. 60
   d. 6

3. You receive an order for 0.2 g of Tigan IM. You have a 5 mL vial labeled 100 mg/mL. How many mL are required?
   a. 0.5
   b. 0.002
   c. 2
   d. 5

4. You check the pharmacy refrigerator and it is 40 degrees Fahrenheit. What is the temperature in degrees Celsius?
   a. 4
   b. −4
   c. 104
   d. 72

5. How many mg of phenobarbital are in one tablet of 2 grain phenobarbital?
   a. 65
   b. 6.5
   c. 13
   d. 130

ACTIVITY 13-1: Case Study—Kilograms

Instructions: Read the following scenario and then answer the critical thinking questions.

Mrs. Sarnoto is probably one of the world's best mothers. In addition to her three biological children, she has adopted four boys. Her days are full of chores, activities, driving, and homework, but many people say Mrs. Sarnoto would not have it any other way.

Mrs. Sarnoto also takes care of all the children's healthcare needs, from vaccinations to outbreaks of poison oak exposure. For this reason, she is a frequent visitor at the retail pharmacy where you work. Over the past five years alone, she has probably purchased at least half of the products in the pharmacy.

As luck would have it, five of the seven children have come down with a terrible bronchial infection. Everyone in the household is miserable, including Mrs. Sarnoto, who is also sick. She knows she has to be the strong one, though, and heads to the pharmacy to fill the amoxicillin prescriptions she has gotten for the family. Each person weighs a different amount and the amoxicillin prescription doses are based on weight in the following formula: 40 mg/kg/day in divided doses every 8 hours. The amoxicillin you have available in the pharmacy is 250 mg/5 mL.

1. One of the children weighs 28 pounds. How much amoxicillin suspension (in mL) will this child receive for a 7-day course of treatment?

2. One of the children weighs 83 pounds. How much amoxicillin suspension (in mL) will this child receive for each dose?

3. Mrs. Sarnoto has been prescribed amoxicillin capsules 500 mg three times daily, but she has a sore throat and wants the suspension. How much suspension (in mL) does she need to complete a 10-day course of treatment?

4. Mrs. Sarnoto had to travel 3 kilometers to get to the pharmacy. How many miles is her round trip?

ACTIVITY 13-2: Case Study—Milliliters

Instructions: Read the following scenario and then answer the critical thinking questions.

Carlene is the most experienced IV pharmacy technician at the Children's Hospital on the hill. She has been making IVs of all types for more than 11 years. She is in charge of all the specialty formulations that require precise measuring of multiple ingredients. Carlene takes great pride in what she does and shares all the little tricks she knows with the other pharmacy technicians who mix IVs. She has found a way to manipulate fluids when measuring so that they come out with exactly the volume the doctor has ordered, regardless of the IV contents. Some of the tricks she has learned include ways to use milliliters and liter measurements interchangeably, taking into account displacement of added items.

1. From a 2.5 liter volume, Carlene removes 325 mL. What is the final volume in mL?

2. Carlene adds 6,700 mL to a volume of 2 liters. How many total liters are there?

3. A formulation of 3.2 liters requires Carlene to remove 1,600 mL of fluid. How many mL are left after this?

ACTIVITY 13-3: Case Study—Drug Storage

Instructions: Read the following scenario and then answer the critical thinking questions.

Note: False medication names are used in this case study.

Sam is the inventory pharmacy technician at one of the biggest compounding pharmacies in his home town. He is in charge of medication purchasing, rotation, budget, and destruction, to name just a few of his tasks. His inventory is very large, accommodating more than 10,000 types of drugs in various forms.

Many of the drugs used for compounding in Sam's pharmacy are in raw and bulk forms. This is the optimum mixing in the situations that constantly arise in this type of business. Proper storage of medication is very important to prevent the breakdown of the active components in each medication. With the volume of inventory Sam has to manage, it is difficult to remember the storage instructions for each medication or product, so he refers to storage data books in each section of the pharmacy.

It is the end-of-the-year inventory and all items must be counted. In addition to counting all the products, Sam uses this time to ensure that all medications are stored within their optimum temperature ranges. For some medications, the manufacturers periodically issue updates on storage instructions.

1. The product ectium is a fine powder that must be kept in a temperature-controlled environment of 40–48 degrees Fahrenheit. What is this temperature in degrees Celsius?

2. Another product, silicutitum, is composed of small 4 cm balls that will melt if left at a temperature above 55 degrees Fahrenheit. What is this temperature in degrees Celsius?

3. A liquid known as pasitoxel will release a vapor if stored in an area above 3.333 degrees Celsius. What is this temperature in degrees Fahrenheit?

4. The lab where the mixing takes place is kept at a steady 72 degrees Fahrenheit. When the staff need to mix basculum, they have to drop the temperature by 11.11 degrees Celsius. After the reduction for mixing basculum, what is the lab temperature in degrees Fahrenheit?

Chapter 14
Dosage Calculations

After completing Chapter 14 from the textbook, you should be able to:	Related Activity in the Workbook/Lab Manual
1. Calculate the correct number of doses in a prescription.	Review Questions Pharmacy Calculation Problems PTCB Exam Practice Questions Activity 14-1, Activity 14-2
2. Determine the quantity to dispense for a prescription.	Review Questions Pharmacy Calculation Problems PTCB Exam Practice Questions Activity 14-1, Activity 14-2, Activity 14-3
3. Calculate the amount of active ingredient in a prescription.	Review Questions Pharmacy Calculation Problems PTCB Exam Practice Questions
4. Determine the correct days supply for a prescription.	Review Questions Pharmacy Calculation Problems PTCB Exam Practice Questions Activity 14-1, Activity 14-2
5. Perform multiple dosage calculations for a single prescription.	Review Questions Pharmacy Calculation Problems PTCB Exam Practice Questions Activity 14-2, Activity 14-3
6. Calculate accurate dosages for pediatric patients.	Review Questions Pharmacy Calculation Problems PTCB Exam Practice Questions Activity 14-1
7. Convert a patient's weight from pounds to kilograms.	Review Questions Pharmacy Calculation Problems PTCB Exam Practice Questions Activity 14-1
8. Perform dosage calculations based upon mg/kg/day.	Review Questions Pharmacy Calculation Problems PTCB Exam Practice Questions

INTRODUCTION

Proper dosing of medications is important to ensure patient safety. Dosage calculations include calculating the number of doses and dispensing quantities and ingredient quantities. These calculations are performed in the pharmacy on a daily basis. As a pharmacy technician, you must have a full working knowledge of how to perform these calculations. To perform dosage calculations, you will draw upon the knowledge you have mastered in previous chapters in the textbook, such as setting up ratios and proportions, keeping like units consistent, and cross-multiplying to solve for an unknown.

REVIEW QUESTIONS

Match the following.

1. _____ Clark's Rule
2. _____ dispensing quantity
3. _____ dose
4. _____ Fried's Rule
5. _____ days supply

a. pediatric dose based on age in months
b. number of days the medication will last
c. pediatric dose based on weight
d. total amount of medication to be given
e. amount of medication taken at one time

Write the correct sig. codes.

6. every 6 hours _____________
7. every day _____________
8. 4 times daily _____________
9. every other day _____________
10. twice daily _____________
11. every 8 hours _____________
12. as needed _____________
13. every 4 hours _____________
14. every 12 hours _____________
15. every 4–6 hours _____________
16. 6 times daily _____________
17. 3 times daily _____________
18. 4–6 times each day _____________

Choose the best answer.

19. When figuring the quantity to dispense you should always:
    a. round up, so the patient gets enough medication.
    b. round down, so the patient will not overdose.
    c. dispense the exact quantity, including a $\frac{1}{2}$ tablet if necessary.
    d. not worry too much about quantity if the patient has refills.

20. A 5 mL bottle of eyedrops will last how long if the patient is using 1 gtt OU bid?
    a. 30
    b. 25
    c. 20
    d. 15

Fill in the blanks.

Mr. Mestophel has a prescription for cephalexin 500 mg, #60, with the sig code "1 po bid ud."

21. The dose is _____________ capsules.
22. The days supply is _____________days.
23. The daily dose is _____________ mg.
24. The dispensing quantity is _____________.
25. If Tyra's emergency inhaler contains 200 puffs and she uses 1 puff up to 4 times daily, how long should her inhaler normally last? _____________

PHARMACY CALCULATION PROBLEMS

Calculate the following.

1. How many grams are in a 4 fl. oz. bottle of levetiracetam 100 mg/mL oral solution?

2. A patient takes 2 teaspoonfuls of citalopram hydrobromide 2 mg/mL. How many mcg are in each dose?

3. A medical order states that a patient is to receive 2 mg/kg/day of a medication. The patient weighs 185 lbs. How many milligrams will the patient receive?

4. A child needs a medication that does not have a pediatric formula available. The usual adult dosage for this medication is 800 mg. If the child weighs 60 lbs, how many mg would constitute an appropriate pediatric dose?

5. A patient weighing 215 lbs is receiving a medication dosed at 5 mcg/kg/day in three divided doses. How many mcg are in each dose?

PTCB EXAM PRACTICE QUESTIONS

1. A prescription reads: Amoxicillin 250 mg/10 mL, 1 tsp bid × 10d. How many mL will you need to dispense?
   a. 50
   b. 100
   c. 150
   d. 200

2. The doctor orders vancomycin 10 mg/kg q12h IV for a newborn. The infant weighs 4,000 g. How many mg should be given per dose?
   a. 18.2
   b. 80
   c. 4
   d. 40

3. Calculate a single dose, in milliliters, for a 22-pound child receiving gentamicin 2 mg/kg of body weight IVPB q8h. Gentamicin is available in 20 mg/2 mL concentration.
   a. 2
   b. 10
   c. 15
   d. 20

4. You have a prescription for Vioxx® 25 mg/5 mL, dispense 150 mL. The patient is to take 12.5 mg once daily. What is the days supply for this prescription?
   a. 60
   b. 30
   c. 6
   d. 15

5. A parent of a 5-year-old child weighing 47 lbs needs to give an oral dose of Tylenol® elixir. The literature states that the dose for a child of this age and weight should not exceed 70 mg/kg per day. This daily maximum is to be divided into six doses. Tylenol® elixir contains 125 mg/5 mL. How many teaspoonfuls would the parent give for a single dose?
   a. 1
   b. 1.25
   c. 1.5
   d. 2

ACTIVITY 14-1: Case Study—Pediatric Dosing

Instructions: Read the following scenario and then answer the critical thinking questions.

Jimmie is a cute 8-year-old boy who weighs 55 pounds and presents with all the symptoms of a cold. The primary symptoms he exhibits are a fever and constant tugging at his ears. The doctor diagnoses acute otitis media and prescribes a 7-day course of amoxicillin capsules and acetaminophen for fever.

As Jimmie is waiting in the lobby with his mother to have his prescription filled, you notice that in spite of his illness, he is quite actively chewing and pulling on his gum. Cute as he is, his gum-smacking is annoying other patients, so the pharmacy attempts to expedite his prescription.

When Jimmie's mother hands the prescription to you, you notice that the doctor has forgotten to write in the dose.

1. What does the pharmacist need to know to correctly dose the amoxicillin for Jimmie?

____

____

____

____

2. While turning the prescription in, the mother mentions that Jimmie's throat is very sore and he has had a hard time swallowing. You realize that capsules will be too difficult for the boy to swallow. How is Jimmie going to take his medicine?

3. The dose turns out to be 500 mg 3 times daily (one capsule). If you were to provide a suspension of 250 mg/5 mL, how much would Jimmie receive per dose, and how much would you need to dispense for the full seven days?

ACTIVITY 14-2: Case Study—Tablets

Instructions: Read the following scenario and then answer the critical thinking questions.

Ms. Kelsey, two-time award-winning journalist, has worked for the newspaper for more than 22 years. She absolutely loves her job because of the places it has taken her and the people she has met. Ms. Kelsey has interviewed so many different people that it truly has made her feel like she has lived a rewarding life.

Ms. Kelsey has taken one particular medication all through her life in tablet form. She has a form of asthma and this medication helps her breathe. In addition to this one tablet, she has a rescue inhaler. A few times in the past she has been treated with maintenance inhalers, but luckily does not have to be on them most of the time. The tablets seem to work very well. Occasionally, depending on age and situation, her doctor has increased or decreased the amount of medication in the tablets to prevent flare-ups.

1. In her 20s, Ms. Kelsey was instructed to take 3 tablets twice a day for 28 days at a time. How many tablets did she need to complete one course of treatment?

2. When she turned 30 years of age, Ms. Kelsey was instructed to take 3.5 tablets 3 times a day for 28 days. How many tablets did she need for one course of treatment?

3. Now that Ms. Kelsey is over 40 years of age, she is instructed to take 3.75 tablets twice a day for 34 days. How many does she need to complete this course of treatment?

4. When Ms. Kelsey turns 50 years old, she will need to take 272 tablets over 32 days with twice-daily dosing. How many tablets will she be taking per dose?

ACTIVITY 14-3: Case Study—Cream

Instructions: Read the following scenario and then answer the critical thinking questions.

Note: False medication names are used in this case study.

Sharla is a very beautiful and active 16-year-old girl. She is captain of her high school cheerleading team, has played the lead role in three of the school's plays this year, and is taking classes for a future career in modeling. Sharla takes exceptionally good care of her body and skin from the inside out, so it was quite disturbing for her when one day she noticed that her slight acne had begun to worsen.

During her teenage years, Sharla has had periodic face and skin conditions resulting from sensitive skin. It turns out that she is very sensitive to detergents, soaps, lotions, and perfumes. It is very difficult for her to keep the rashes under control when she breaks the rules and wears perfume for special occasions such as school dances.

Sharla has received prescriptions from the compounding pharmacy for all types of perfume-free creams over the years. Almost all have helped, and she uses this pharmacy exclusively for all new formulations she is prescribed. She has received some prescriptions in heavy jars or small tubes depending on the area to be treated.

1. When Sharla had a round, mild rash on her bottom left cheek, she was prescribed listfal 34 g and palfite 16 g combined. How many mg is this?

2. When her legs were covered in a rash, Sharla was prescribed 12 pounds of crexopen cream. How much is this in ounces?

3. For the mild hypersensitive reaction just under her ear, she was prescribed junisten 1.2 kilograms. How many ounces is this?

CHAPTER 15
Concentrations and Dilutions

After completing Chapter 15 from the textbook, you should be able to:	Related Activity in the Workbook/Lab Manual
1. Calculate weight/weight concentrations.	Review Questions Pharmacy Calculation Problems PTCB Exam Practice Questions
2. Calculate weight/volume concentrations.	Review Questions Pharmacy Calculation Problems PTCB Exam Practice Questions Activity 15-1, Activity 15-2,
3. Calculate volume/volume concentrations.	Review Questions Pharmacy Calculation Problems PTCB Exam Practice Questions Activity 15-1
4. Calculate dilutions of stock solutions.	Review Questions Pharmacy Calculation Problems PTCB Exam Practice Questions

INTRODUCTION

Concentrations and dilutions, which can feel overwhelming and intimidating, are really no more than a series of simple ratios and proportions. Concentrations of many pharmaceutical preparations are expressed as a percent strength. Percent strength represents how many grams of active ingredient are in 100 mL. In the case of solids such as ointments, percent strength represents the number of grams of active ingredient contained in 100 g. Percent strength can be reduced to a fraction or to a decimal, which may be useful in solving these calculations. It is best to convert any ratio strengths to a percent. As a pharmacy technician, you will use concentrations and dilutions in a variety of pharmacy practice settings, so it is important that you master this skill.

REVIEW QUESTIONS

Match the following.

1. _____ concentration
2. _____ diluent
3. _____ percent strength
4. _____ % volume/volume
5. _____ % weight/volume
6. _____ % weight/weight

a. percent strength concentration of a liquid active ingredient contained within a liquid base
b. percent strength concentration of a solid active ingredient contained within a solid base
c. percent strength concentration of a solid active ingredient contained within a liquid base
d. refers to the strength of active pharmaceutical ingredient in a medication.
e. representation of the number of grams of active ingredient contained in 100 mL
f. a substance used to dilute another substance

True or False?

7. Grams and milliliters are used interchangeably in concentration problems, depending on whether you are working with solids in grams or liquids in milliliters, as they are considered equivalent measures.
   T F

8. To accurately perform w/v concentration calculations, the proportion must be set up as grams over mL.
   T F

9. When mixing powders with liquids, the liquid (base) quantity is considered the total quantity, as the powder will either dissolve or suspend within the base liquid.
   T F

Choose the best answer.

10. To prevent errors while documenting quantities, what is the rule when it comes to decimals?
    a. Never use a fraction stated as a decimal.
    b. Be sure to have the product in stock.
    c. Always use the number 0 before any fraction.
    d. Only use whole numbers.

11. How many 500 mg metronidazole tablets will be needed to compound the following prescription for a patient? "Metronidazole 3%, suspending agent 30%, simple syrup 40% qsad H_2O to 150 mL."
    a. 9
    b. 7
    c. 10
    d. 18

12. You get in a prescription for "Amoxil 400 mg po tid × 10 days." Your pharmacy has in stock an Amoxil® oral suspension 250 mg/5 mL. What is the exact volume of medication you will need to correctly and completely fill the prescription for the patient?
    a. 150 mL
    b. 168 mL
    c. 240 mL
    d. 200 mL

13. How many grams of 2% silver nitrate ointment will deliver 1 gram of the active ingredient?
    a. 25 g
    b. 4 g
    c. 50 g
    d. 20 g

14. What volume of 5% aluminum acetate solution will be needed if 120 mL of 0.05% solution are extemporaneously compounded for patient use?
    a. 12 mL
    b. 1.2 mL
    c. 8.3 mL
    d. 0.83 mL

15. Calculate the flow rate in drops per minute if a physician orders D5W/NS 1,400 mL over 12 hours using an administration set that delivers 40 gtts/mL.
    a. 87 gtts/min
    b. 68 gtts/min
    c. 117 gtts/min
    d. 78 gtts/min

16. 325 mg could also be written as:
    a. 2 gr.
    b. 5 gr.
    c. 10 gr.
    d. 1/2 gr.

17. From the following formula, calculate in kilograms the quantity of miconazole needed to prepare 12 kg of powder.

    zinc oxide 1 part

    calamine 2 parts

    miconazole 1.5 parts

    bismuth subgallate 3 parts

    talcum 8 parts

    a. 15.5
    b. 0.097
    c. 1.16
    d. 1.5

18. Calculate the flow rate for an IV of 1,000 mL to run in over 8 hours with a set calibrated at 20 gtt/mL.
    a. 41.6 gtt/min
    b. 17.36 gtt/min
    c. 125.1 gtt/min
    d. 50 gtt/min

PHARMACY CALCULATION PROBLEMS

Calculate the following.

1. How many grams of drug are contained in 500 mL of a 20% solution?

2. A technician needs to compound metoclopramide suspension 5 mg/5 mL, qsad 100 mL. Metoclopramide is available in 10 mg tablets. How many tablets will you need to triturate for this compound?

3. What is the percent strength of a solution that is made by adding 200 mL of sterile water to 600 mL of a 25% solution?

4. If a technician is compounding a 5% hydrocortisone emulsion in 120 g of aquaphilic ointment, how many grams of hydrocortisone powder will she need?

5. How many grams of active ingredient are in 500 milliliters of a 1:20 solution?

PTCB EXAM PRACTICE QUESTIONS

1. You have 200 mL of a 30% solution. You dilute the solution to 600 mL. What is the percent strength of the final solution?
   a. 60
   b. 30
   c. 12
   d. 10

2. A solution of ampicillin contains 250 mg/mL. What is the percent strength of the solution?
   a. 2.5
   b. 25
   c. 12.5
   d. 15.2

3. How many grams of amino acid are in 500 mL of 8.5% solution?
   a. 64.3
   b. 42.5
   c. 16
   d. 8.5

4. Neostigmine is available in a 1:1000 concentration in a 20 mL vial. You have a prescription for 16 mg. How many mL are required?
   a. 1.6
   b. 16
   c. 12.5
   d. 1.2

5. Epinephrine is available as a 1:1000 w/v solution. If the patient dose is 0.2 mg IM, how many mL are needed?
   a. 2
   b. 1
   c. 0.2
   d. 0.1

ACTIVITY 15-1: Case Study—Dosing

Instructions: Read the following scenario and then answer the critical thinking questions.

Wintertime brings a barrage of colds throughout the Hudson family. They are a very active family of Dad, Mom, two boys (11 and 14) and two girls (8 and 12). Each child participates in at least one winter sport, keeping them on the go. The children spend a lot of time riding to games with other families and their parents think this makes it easier to pick up infections. Although they manage to avoid most ailments year round, three weeks in January of each year seem to bring an assortment of infection bugs to this household. This past winter was no exception.

When January rolled around, the infections hit this family like dominoes. The pattern is almost the same every year. Once everyone was sick at the same time and everyone received treatments for different bacterial infections.

1. Dad received cefotetan in either 1 g or 2 g for IM injection. The 1 g vial would be mixed with 2 mL sterile water and the 2 g would be mixed with 3 mL of sterile water. What is the concentration of the 1 g and the 2 g cefotetan with these diluent amounts?

____

____

____

____

2. Mom is going to receive a Zithromax® suspension 500 mg per day for 1 day, then 250 mg per day for 4 days. The concentration available to you is 200 mg/5 mL. How many teaspoonfuls does Mom receive per dose on day 1? How many on day 2?

____

____

____

____

3. The 8-year-old girl weighs 42 lbs. and will receive Unasyn® at 300 mg/kg/day. How much is her dose per day?

____

____

____

____

4. The 14-year-old boy is going to receive ceftriaxone 2 g IV daily for 3 days, to be infused over 30 minutes. For a 2 g dose, 19.2 mL of sterile water were added to the vial and the medication was then injected into a 100 mL bag of NS. How many mL/min are infused if the total volume of the piggyback has to empty out over 30 minutes?

____

____

____

____

ACTIVITY 15-2: Case Study—Reconstitution

Instructions: Read the following scenario and then answer the critical thinking questions.

Jeremy is a 24-year-old recent graduate of the pharmacy technician program at the community college. This is his first job in pharmacy and within 6 months he is already being trained to make small preparations in the sterile preparation area of the home infusion pharmacy where he is employed. Training in this area begins with practicing reconstitution techniques for a while and then moving up to larger volumes.

In the course of the workday, Jeremy makes a lot of low-volume products that are less than 50 mL. Jeremy enjoys his work and is especially happy with the fact that he gets to apply the knowledge he obtained in school. For the most part, the medications he works with in this pharmacy use sterile water as the main diluent. Jeremy works with any number of powder medications in vials, all of which he needs to reconstitute.

1. Jeremy has a 1 g vial of vancomycin and adds 10 mL of sterile water. What is the final concentration of the vancomycin?

____

____

____

____

2. If Jeremy were to add 20 mL sterile water to this vancomycin, what would be the final concentration?

____

____

____

____

3. What is the final concentration if Jeremy had 2 g of vancomycin and he added 20 mL sterile water to this vial?

____

____

____

____

ACTIVITY 15-3: Case Study—Concentration

Instructions: Read the following scenario and then answer the critical thinking questions.

Note: False medication names are used in this case study.

Renee is a clinical pharmacy technician at a mid-sized hospital with about 120 patient beds. This bed count includes a small 20-bed unit that is for patients who require a little longer stay for rehabilitation purposes. Typically these patients are a little older and less mobile than patients who are in the hospital for routine surgical needs. Many of these patients move on to some sort of assisted living situation, such as community apartment homes where part-time nursing care is available.

Part of the care the nurses provide to these patients is the administration of medications such as IV infusions, insulin shots (for the squeamish), and other types of injections (such as cyanocobalamin). Other nurses occasionally have to do careful calculation and administration of pain medications in suspension or injectable forms.

Part of Renee's job is to help provide the medications to nursing for patient administration; this includes mixing of unit-dose preparations such as injectables or oral liquids. In addition, Renee helps double-check all the calculations, as part of a safety check. Because she works in pharmacy, Renee also knows what drug forms and strengths are immediately available.

1. Bascoletine is available as 30 mg/mL in a 15 mL vial. How many total mg are available in this vial?

2. If the nurse withdrew one-quarter of the vial contents for a dose, how many mgs would be in that dose?

3. The doctor prescribes the entire vial of medication from question #1, divided into 5 equal doses. How many mg and mL would each dose have?

4. Using the medication information from question #1, how many mg are in 5 mL?

CHAPTER 16

Alligations

After completing Chapter 16 from the textbook, you should be able to:	Related Activity in the Workbook/Lab Manual
1. Understand when to use the alligation principle for calculations.	Review Questions Pharmacy Calculation Problems PTCB Exam Practice Questions Activity 16-1, Activity 16-2, Activity 16-3
2. Calculate and solve a variety of alligation-related problems.	Review Questions Pharmacy Calculation Problems PTCB Exam Practice Questions Activity 16-1, Activity 16-2, Activity 16-3

INTRODUCTION

The alligation method is used in the pharmacy when it is necessary to mix two products that have different percent strengths of the same active ingredient. The strength of the final product will fall between the strengths of each original product. Although these calculations can be confusing at first, once you master the alligation grid, you should be able to perform these calculations easily.

REVIEW QUESTIONS

Fill in the blanks.

1. Solvents and diluents such as water, vanishing cream base, and white petrolatum are considered a percent strength of ____________.
2. Liquids, including solutions, syrups, elixirs, and even lotions, are expressed in ____________.
3. Solids are expressed in ____________. These include powders, creams, and ointments.
4. The alligation formula requires that you express the strength as a ____________ when setting up the problem.
5. When writing percents or using decimals, always use a leading ____________.
6. 1 fl. oz. is commonly rounded to ____________ mL.
7. 1 avoirdupois oz. is commonly rounded to ____________ g.
8. The ____________ strength goes in the top left box of an alligation grid.
9. The ____________ strength goes in the bottom left box of an alligation grid.
10. The ____________ goes in the center box of an alligation grid.

Use alligations to answer the following questions.

You have one gallon of silver nitrate 1% stock solution, which you can dilute with distilled water. How many milliliters of each will you need to make 1 L of silver nitrate 0.25% solution?

11. ____________ mL of the 1% stock solution
12. ____________ mL of distilled water

You have hydrocortisone 10% ointment and hydrocortisone 2% ointment. How many grams of each will you use to prepare hydrocortisone 5% ointment 120 g?

13. ____________ g of the 10% ointment
14. ____________ g of the 2% ointment

Prepare 480 mL of a 1:30 solution using a 1:10 solution and a 1:50 solution.

15. ____________ mL of the 1:50 solution
16. ____________ mL of the 1:10 solution
17. How many grams of 10% ointment should you add to 20 g of 2% ointment to make 5% ointment? ____________ g
18. How many milliliters of water should you add to 50 mL of betadine 0.25% solution to prepare betadine 1:1000 solution? ____________ mL
19. How many grams of lidocaine 2% ointment should you mix with 22.5 g of lidocaine 10% ointment to prepare lidocaine 5% ointment 2 oz.? ____________ g
20. Convert 25% to a ratio strength. ____________
21. 1:2 is what percentage strength? ____________

Fill in the blanks.

22. 1:2 50% 0.50 ____________
23. ____________ 33% 0.33 $\frac{1}{3}$
24. 3:4 ____________ 0.75 $\frac{3}{4}$
25. 1:1 100% ____________ 1

PHARMACY CALCULATION PROBLEMS

Calculate the following.

1. A technician is compounding 16 ounces of zinc oxide 7.5% ointment. In stock, there is zinc oxide 20% ointment and petroleum jelly. How many ounces of each will the technician need to make the final product?

2. You have to compound 1 liter of a 4% solution. The pharmacy has a 12% solution and a 2% solution in stock. How many milliliters of each will be needed to make the final product?

3. You need to prepare a 2% solution from the 10% solution and sterile water that is in stock. Four fluid ounces are required for the prescription. How many milliliters of each (the 10% solution and water) will you need to make the final product?

4. You need 0.5 L of a 2.5% solution for a prescription. The pharmacy has on hand a 1:5 solution and a 1:100 solution. How many milliliters of each will be needed for this compound?

5. A prescription calls for 32 fl. oz. of a 1:1000 solution that is to be compounded. The pharmacy stocks a 1:20 solution and sterile water. How many milliliters of each will be required for this compound?

PTCB EXAM PRACTICE QUESTIONS

1. Calculate how many mL of 50% dextrose solution and how many mL of water are needed to prepare 4.5 L of a 1% solution.
   a. 4,410 mL dextrose and 90 mL water
   b. 500 mL dextrose and 4,000 mL water
   c. 90 mL dextrose and 4,410 mL water
   d. 95 mL dextrose and 4,405 mL water

2. How many mL of a 15% solution of sodium chloride and how many mL of water should be used to prepare 1 liter of a 0.9% solution of sodium chloride?
   a. 60 mL 15% and 940 mL water
   b. 940 mL 15% and 60 mL water
   c. 500 mL 15% and 500 mL water
   d. 200 mL 15% and 800 mL water

3. How many grams of 10% boric acid ointment should be mixed with petrolatum (0%) to prepare 700 g of a 5% boric acid ointment?
   a. 300 g petrolatum and 400 g 10%
   b. 200 g petrolatum and 500 g 10%
   c. 300 g 10% and 400 g petrolatum
   d. 350 g 10% and 350 g petrolatum

4. You are asked to prepare 2.5 liters of a 1:20 solution from a 30% solution and water. How many mL of the 30% solution and how many mL of water are needed?
   a. 500 mL water and 2,000 mL 30% solution
   b. 417 mL 30% solution and 2,083 mL water
   c. 417 mL water and 2,083 mL 30% solution
   d. 2,000 mL water and 500 mL 30% solution

5. Calculate how many mL of 50% dextrose solution and how many mL of 10% dextrose solution are needed to prepare 4.5 L of a 1% solution.
   a. 3,802 mL 50% solution and 698 mL 10% solution
   b. 3,802 mL 10% solution and 698 mL 50% solution
   c. 3.8 mL 50% solution and 0.7 mL 10% solution
   d. 3.8 mL 10% solution and 0.7 mL 50% solution

ACTIVITY 16-1: Case Study—Cream

Instructions: Read the following scenario and then answer the critical thinking questions.

Jerry Rands is hypersensitive to numerous substances, and frequently develops a small rash somewhere on his body. He is not even sure of all the things he is sensitive to! All he knows is that over the course of his lifetime he has had a skin rash at least once a month somewhere on his body. He has been to the pharmacy to purchase anti-itch cream in many different brands and strengths. Jerry's doctor usually advises him to purchase the OTC or prescription-strength product known as hydrocortisone cream.

The time has come again when Jerry develops a small rash and asks the doctor which strength he will need to treat this one. Just like anybody else, Jerry has a small collection of these creams in his medicine cabinet that are still in date and available for use. The problem, however, lies in getting the correct strength when he has only certain amounts of certain strengths. It seems that he does not have enough of the strength the doctor ordered this time, so he wonders if he can mix them.

1. Jerry is to use hydrocortisone 1% cream. All he has available is 2.5% and 0.25%. How many grams of 2.5% hydrocortisone cream should be mixed with 240 g of 0.25% hydrocortisone cream to make 1% hydrocortisone cream?

   ____

   ____

   ____

   ____

2. The doctor tells Jerry to divide the total amount of cream calculated in question #1 into 6 even doses for application. How many grams are in each dose?

   ____

   ____

   ____

   ____

3. What is the total amount of 1% hydrocortisone cream Jerry mixed?

4. Jerry decides to divide the total amount of 1% hydrocortisone cream he has mixed into 2 ounce jars. How many jars does he need?

ACTIVITY 16-2: Case Study—Gelcaps

Instructions: Read the following scenario and then answer the critical thinking questions.

Maryann works in a mid-sized veterinarian compounding pharmacy. Each day brings something new and creative. She may receive an order for suppositories for medium-size rodents or syringes filled with antibiotics for baby birds. Maryann's job requires her to have solid math skills and excellent aseptic technique.

Compounding is used to formulate prescriptions when no commercial strength is available—and animal pharmaceuticals are a very narrow field. Compounding medications for animals fills a void in a world where little is known about what works on a grand scale for a general species. More and more information appears every week for new formulations and animal behavior. With these updates occurring constantly, Maryann must stay on top of her education and training to remain an asset to her chosen field.

A major part of Maryann's compounding is the creation of various gelcaps for various medications. It is a very convenient form for most animals, and flavoring is easily added to this drug form under most conditions.

1. The following formula is to make a total of 50 gelcaps. How much of each ingredient is needed to make only 10 gelcaps?

   FORMULA

caffeine	0.6 g
aspirin	2.0 g
inert ingredient	0.25 g

2. How much is needed to make 15 capsules?

3. What is the total number of grams of all 3 ingredients for 20 capsules?

ACTIVITY 16-3: Case Study—Bulk

Instructions: Read the following scenario and then answer the critical thinking questions.

Note: False names are used for the homeopathic substances in this case study.

Part of the day at the homeopathic manufacturing pharmacy where Lynette works is spent mixing large batches of specialty gels for patients who require these large amounts to fill their prescriptions. A variety of herbs is available to Lynette here, and it always smells like a fresh meadow of grass and trees. Lynette has to wear all the appropriate gear, such as gloves and gowns, because the strength of some of these compounds can cause hypersensitivity skin reactions.

As her employer is a small facility, part of Lynette's duties includes the purchasing of the larger-size containers, lids, and packaging tools. It is not uncommon for Lynette to make a 2,000 g jar full of homeopathic gel for muscle aches. All the compounds in this facility come in at least four different strengths.

1. Lynette is making histkatel crucious gel for muscle fatigue. She needs to have a 6% final concentration. How many grams of 10% histkatel crucious gel should be mixed with 1,800 g of 5% histkatel crucious gel to make the 6% gel?

2. How much is the total amount of histkatel crucious gel compounded?

3. How many pounds does this total add up to?

4. Lynette is to package the bulk gel into as few 8 ounce sealed jars as she can. How many jars does she need?

Chapter 17
Parenteral Calculations

After completing Chapter 17 from the textbook, you should be able to:	Related Activity in the Workbook/Lab Manual
1. Illustrate the principle of basic dimensional analysis.	Review Questions Pharmacy Calculation Problems PTCB Exam Practice Questions Activity 17-1
2. Calculate flow duration for parenteral products.	Review Questions Pharmacy Calculation Problems PTCB Exam Practice Questions Activity 17-1
3. Calculate the volume per hour for parenteral orders.	Review Questions Pharmacy Calculation Problems PTCB Exam Practice Questions
4. Calculate the drug per hour for parenteral products.	Review Questions Pharmacy Calculation Problems PTCB Exam Practice Questions
5. Calculate drip rates in both drops/minute and milliliters/hour.	Review Questions Pharmacy Calculation Problems PTCB Exam Practice Questions
6. Calculate TPN milliequivalents.	Review Questions Pharmacy Calculation Problems PTCB Exam Practice Questions

INTRODUCTION

The preparation and administration of parenteral products, such as IVs, infusions, TPN, and chemotherapy, require the performance of specific calculations. It is common for individuals to become overwhelmed and confused when approaching complex pharmacy calculations. The truth is, however, that although many pharmacy calculations appear to be complex, they are in actuality very simple. Often described as the most difficult and challenging calculations used in pharmacy, parenteral calculations, drip rates and TPN milliequivalents are all solved with basic, fundamental math and arithmetic skills. The use of proportions, cross-multiplication, and dimensional analysis will aid you in performing virtually all parenteral calculations that you will need to solve as a pharmacy technician.

REVIEW QUESTIONS

Match the following.

1. drop factor
2. drops per minute
3. mg/hr
4. flow rates
5. flow rate duration
6. hypertonic solutions
7. isotonic solutions
8. hypotonic solutions
9. IV infusion
10. micro drip
11. TPN
12. mL/hr

a. solutions that have osmotic pressure equal to that of cell contents
b. length of time over which an IV will be administered
c. amount of fluid to be administered intravenously per hour
d. term describing a number of pharmacy calculations used in the preparation of IV infusions
e. dose that will be administered per hour of infusion
f. solution made to replenish many of the body's basic nutritional needs via parenteral administration
g. compounded solution that provides fluids, specific medications, nutrients, electrolytes, and minerals
h. volume of medication to be administered per minute
i. solutions that have greater osmotic pressure than cell contents
j. solutions that have a lower osmotic pressure than cell contents
k. abbreviated listing referring to a specific drip rate
l. most commonly used drip rate; 60 gtts/mL

Solve the following problems.

13. A 2 L IV bag is being administered at a rate of 400 mL per hour. How long will this IV bag last? __________
14. A 2 L IV is to be administered at 500 mL/hr. How long will the IV last? __________
15. A patient is set to start a 250 mL infusion of amoxicillin in lactated Ringers 5% at noon. The bag is to be administered at a rate of 125 mL per hour. At what time will the infusion be complete? __________
16. Three 500 mL IV bags are to be infused at a rate of 150 mL per hour. How long will these three bags last? __________
17. Three 2 L IV bags containing ciprofloxacin and NS are set to be administered at a rate of 250 mL per hour at 1:00 p.m. When will all three bags be completely administered? __________
18. A patient is to receive 500 mL infused over 2 hours. What is the rate of infusion in mL per hour? __________

19. A 500 mL IV, containing 2 mg of Toradol®, is to be given over 100 minutes. What is the rate of infusion in mL per hour? ____________

20. 500 mL of D5W containing 1 g of lidocaine hydrochloride is to be given over 250 minutes. What is the infusion rate in mL per hour? ____________

PHARMACY CALCULATION PROBLEMS

Calculate the following.

1. How many hours will a 2 L bag of TPN last if it is scheduled to run at 90 mL/hr?

2. A bag of heparin IV with a concentration of 25,000 units/250 mL is to be hung for a patient. How many units per hour will the patient receive if the solution is infusing at 50 mL/hr?

3. What is the flow rate in mL/hr for vancomycin 1 g/250 mL IV, if it is to infuse over 90 minutes?

4. What is the flow rate in gtts/min for 100 mL of an antifungal to be administered over 60 minutes? The tubing is calibrated at 60 gtts/mL.

5. If a 1 L bag of D5NS with 20 KCl is hung at 0700, when will the new bag be due if it is running at 125 mL/hr?

PTCB EXAM PRACTICE QUESTIONS

1. If a 1 liter bag of D5W is run through an IV into a patient's arm over 8 hours, what is the rate of infusion in mL/hr?
   a. 100
   b. 10
   c. 12.5
   d. 125

2. If a 1,000 mL bag of normal saline is run at 100 mL/hr, how long will the bag last?
   a. 8
   b. 10
   c. 12
   d. 6

3. If the infusion rate for an IV is 80 mL/hr and it is run for $4\frac{1}{2}$ hours, how many mL has the patient received?
   a. 300
   b. 320
   c. 360
   d. 380

4. How many drops per minute will a patient receive if an IV of 1,000 mL of 5% dextrose injection is run in over 8 hours? The drip factor is 15 drops/mL.
   a. 8
   b. 16
   c. 32
   d. 43

5. You receive an order for heparin IV to infuse at 1,000 units per hour. What will be the flow rate in mL/hr for a 500 mL bag of D5W with 25,000 units of heparin?
   a. 20
   b. 10
   c. 2
   d. 1

ACTIVITY 17-1: Case Study—Iron Dextran

Instructions: Read the following scenario and then answer the critical thinking questions.

After arguing with his then-girlfriend of whom his family did not approve, Philip drove away from the house in an angry state. He is certain now that he was not in the right frame of mind to be driving that night. The car spun out of control on a fairly isolated road and hit a tree. Eventually, Philip made it out alive, but he spent 12 weeks in the hospital recuperating. He did not call his family as he probably should have, because the last time he spoke to them, things ended on bad terms. It has now been 8 months since the accident, and Philip has not seen his family during that time. He is reuniting with them now to discuss the accident because he had decided that it would help him heal emotionally.

Philip was lucky to have made it back to health. He suffered a concussion, a fractured arm, and multiple bruises. The doctors told him he lost a lot of blood, but he is not exactly sure from what part of his body or how much. Philip received excellent care at the major medical center, where he recalls being on numerous medications. Now all his family members are sharing stories of various hospital stays, and the discussion turns to the medications they recall getting, especially the IVs that hung on the poles while they were inpatients. Philip recalls one, called iron dextran, being "really black."

1. The first dose of iron dextran that Philip received was a test dose of 25 mg in 100 mL NS infused over 20 minutes. What was the concentration of this piggyback?

   ____

   ____

   ____

   ____

2. What was the infusion rate per minute for this test dose of iron dextran?

   ____

   ____

   ____

   ____

3. Philip's total daily dose of iron dextran became 1 g, mixed in a 1 L bag of NS and infused over 8 hours. What was the rate per hour?

4. Using the same information as in question #3, how much iron dextran did Philip receive per hour?

CHAPTER 18
Dosage Formulations and Administration

After completing Chapter 18 from the textbook, you should be able to:	Related Activity in the Workbook/Lab Manual
1. Explain drug nomenclature.	Review Questions
2. Define medication error.	Review Questions
3. List and explain the rights of medication administration.	Review Questions
4. Identify various dosage formulations.	Review Questions, PTCB Exam Practice Questions
5. Identify the advantages and disadvantages of solid and liquid medication dosage formulations.	Review Questions, PTCB Exam Practice Questions
6. Explain the differences between solutions, emulsions, and suspensions.	Review Questions, PTCB Exam Practice Questions
7. Explain the difference between ointments and creams.	Review Questions, PTCB Exam Practice Questions
8. Identify the various routes of administration and give examples of each.	Review Questions, PTCB Exam Practice Questions
9. Give examples of common medications for various routes of administration.	Review Questions
10. Identify the advantages and disadvantages of each route of administration.	Review Questions
11. Identify the parenteral routes of administration.	Review Questions, PTCB Exam Practice Questions
12. Explain the difference between transdermal and topical routes of administration.	Review Questions, PTCB Exam Practice Questions
13. Explain the difference between sublingual and buccal routes of administration.	Review Questions, PTCB Exam Practice Questions
14. Identify the abbreviations for the common routes of administration and dosage formulations.	Review Questions

INTRODUCTION

As a pharmacy technician, one of your many responsibilities is to work with the pharmacist to prepare and dispense medications to patients. You need to know that drugs can come from one of three sources: natural, synthetic, or genetically engineered.

You also need to understand the concept of drug nomenclature and how to recognize a drug's chemical, generic, and trade/brand names. Finally, you must be familiar with the meaning of and use for each dosage form and route. Most of the dosage forms do imply a certain route that is to be used. However, many dosage forms may be administered via several different routes. For example, a tablet is commonly administered orally, but it can be administered vaginally as well. Liquid medications can also be administered in a variety of ways. If the prescription order is not clear as to the dosage form and route, the pharmacy staff and medical staff must work together to determine what is best for the patient and to avoid medication errors.

REVIEW QUESTIONS

Match the following.

1._____ anhydrous
2._____ aromatic
3._____ aqueous
4._____ dosage form
5._____ emollient
6._____ emulsion
7._____ formulary
8._____ HMO
9._____ homogenous
10._____ hydrophobic
11._____ nomenclature
12._____ occlusive
13._____ oleaginous
14._____ route of administration
15._____ synthesized
16._____ semi-synthetic
17._____ synthetic
18._____ viscous
19._____ volatile

a. actual form of the drug
b. listing of drugs approved for use
c. a group having all the same qualities
d. evaporates rapidly
e. set of names; way of naming
f. without water
g. thick; almost jelly-like
h. containing oil; has oil-like properties
i. having a fragrant aroma
j. a naturally occurring compound that has been chemically altered
k. drug produced in a laboratory to imitate a naturally occurring compound
l. contains water
m. health maintenance organization
n. liquid mixture of water and oil
o. how a drug is introduced into or on the body
p. closes off; keeps air away
q. repels water
r. softening and soothing to the skin
s. drugs that are not naturally occurring in the body

Choose the best answer.

20. Which is not one of the classifications of sources of drugs?
    a. genetically engineered
    b. synthetic
    c. natural
    d. manufactured

21. An advantage of solid-dose medications is:
    a. longer shelf life before expiration.
    b. dosing is more accurate.
    c. patients are able to self-administer.
    d. all of the above.

22. Ointments are:
    a. semisolid.
    b. solid.
    c. semiliquid.
    d. jellyfied.

Match the following drugs with their sources.

23. _____ digoxin
24. _____ aspirin
25. _____ human growth hormone
26. _____ vincristine
27. _____ OxyContin

a. periwinkle
b. foxglove
c. synthetic opium
d. white willow bark
e. pituitary gland

Fill in the blanks.

28. _____________ are solid medications that are compacted into small, formed shapes.
29. _____________ release carbon dioxide when they come into contact with liquid.
30. Also called pastilles or troches, _____________ are a hard, disk-shaped, solid dosage form that contain a sugar base.
31. Oleaginous ointments are _____________ used to soothe and cool the skin or mucous membranes.
32. _____________ are liquid solutions that may be either alcoholic or hydroalcoholic.

PHARMACY CALCULATION PROBLEMS

Calculate the following.

1. Levetiracetam is usually initiated at 20 mg/kg/day in 2 divided doses for a pediatric patient. Determine the dose in milligrams for a boy who weighs 50 pounds.

2. Levetiracetam comes in a 100 mg/mL oral solution. How many milliliters will you need per dose for the patient in question #1?

3. If a patient is receiving ondansetron 4 mg IVP tid prn, what is the maximum daily dosage the patient will receive in milligrams?

4. If an acetaminophen 80 mg suppository is prescribed q4–6 hr prn, what is the maximum number of suppositories the patient can receive in a day?

PTCB EXAM PRACTICE QUESTIONS

1. The best known example of a sublingual tablet formulation is:
   a. hydrochlorothiazide.
   b. nitroglycerin.
   c. digoxin.
   d. codeine.

2. Which would *not* be caused by particulate material in an intravenous injection?
   a. air emboli
   b. thrombus
   c. phlebitis
   d. necrosis

3. Ointments are likely to be used in which route of administration?
   a. oral
   b. buccal
   c. topical
   d. sublingual

4. Which ophthalmic formulation will maintain the drug in contact with the eye the longest?
   a. solution
   b. suspension
   c. gel
   d. ointment

5. What is the term for an injection directly into a joint?
   a. intracardiac
   b. intrapleural
   c. intravitreal
   d. intra-articular

CHAPTER 19

The Body and Drugs

After completing Chapter 19 from the textbook, you should be able to:	Related Activity in the Workbook/Lab Manual
1. Explain the differences between pharmacodynamics and pharmacokinetics.	Review Questions, PTCB Exam Practice Questions
2. Understand the ways in which cell receptors react to drugs.	Review Questions
3. Describe mechanism of action and identify and understand its key factor.	Review Questions
4. Explain how drugs are absorbed, distributed, metabolized, and cleared by the body.	Review Questions, PTCB Exam Practice Questions
5. Explain the difference between fat-soluble and water-soluble drugs and give examples of each.	Review Questions
6. Identify and explain the effect of bioavailability and its relationship to drug effectiveness.	Review Questions
7. Understand addiction and addictive behavior.	Review Questions, PTCB Exam Practice Questions
8. Describe the role of the pharmacy technician in identifying drug-abusing patients.	Review Questions
9. List and identify some drugs that interact with alcohol.	Review Questions

INTRODUCTION

Pharmacology is the study of drugs, including their composition, uses, application, and effects. Although the pharmacist is responsible for using his or her specialized knowledge to provide pharmaceutical care to patients, pharmacy technicians too must understand the basics of pharmacology. *Pharmacodynamics* is the study of how drugs produce their effects on the desired cells and how the drug is then processed by the body. *Pharmacokinetics* is the study of how the body handles drugs, how drugs are changed from their original form into something that the body can use, and how they are eliminated from the body.

REVIEW QUESTIONS

Match the following.

1._____ absorption
2._____ agonist
3._____ bioavailability
4._____ clearance
5._____ dependency
6._____ excretion
7._____ metabolism
8._____ addiction
9._____ tolerance
10._____ metabolites
11._____ half-life
12._____ distribution
13._____ antagonist

a. physical need
b. a drug that prevents receptor activation
c. a drug that activates a receptor
d. how a drug moves from the blood to the site of action
e. how drugs are eliminated
f. compulsive craving or need
g. substance produced by metabolization
h. time required for serum level to decrease by half
i. process of transforming a drug
j. requires larger dose to achieve the same effect
k. the amount of a drug that becomes available
l. how a drug moves from the introduction site to the bloodstream
m. time it takes a drug to be eliminated

Choose the best answer.

14. Pharmacodynamics can be described as the study of:
a. receptors producing a specific effect.
b. what the body does to a drug.
c. the process of drug interactions.
d. how drugs are made.

15. How a drug works is called:
a. effective distribution.
b. chemical process.
c. mechanism of action.
d. potency.

16. An antagonist:
a. is very annoying.
b. produces certain predicted actions.
c. stops a drug from working.
d. neutralizes the effects of narcotics.

17. ED50 refers to the:
a. amount of a drug that produces half the normal response.
b. binding medium used in compounding.
c. effective drug at 50%.
d. top 50 most effective drugs.

18. Once a drug is at a serum concentration of less than 3%, it is considered:
a. nontoxic.
b. out of range.
c. eliminated.
d. ineffective.

19. Which is not a form of excretion?
a. breath
b. sweat
c. urine
d. odor

20. Pinocytosis is a:
    a. form of transportation of drugs into cells.
    b. a medicinally powerful plant.
    c. a rare type of gum disease.
    d. none of the above.

21. Which of the following is not a route of absorption?
    a. stomach lining
    b. blood
    c. urine
    d. cell membranes

22. The rate of administration of a drug is determined by the:
    a. prescriber.
    b. research and development process.
    c. chemical nature of the drug.
    d. health of the patient.

23. Denial is a sign of:
    a. addiction.
    b. dependence.
    c. truth avoidance.
    d. psychological unbalance.

24. Which of these drugs may produce increased heart rate when mixed with alcohol?
    a. hydrocodone
    b. alprazolam
    c. metformin
    d. warfarin

25. Pharmacokinetics is a term for the study of:
    a. receptors producing a specific effect.
    b. the time course of a drug in the body.
    c. the process of drug interactions.
    d. how drugs are made.

True or False?

26. Salts do not matter if the active ingredient is the same.

    T F

27. The absorption of a drug governs the bioavailability of that drug.

    T F

28. Addiction is the same as dependence.

    T F

29. Withdrawal is not difficult if a patient is merely dependent on a drug.

    T F

30. When a person constantly needs a higher dose of a drug, it is a sure sign that the patient is an addict.

    T F

PHARMACY CALCULATION PROBLEMS

Calculate the following.

1. On Wednesdays, a pharmacy offers a 10% discount for senior citizens on all their prescription and over-the-counter medications. How much would a person save if she purchased $219 worth of medications?

2. A man has brought in a prescription for ranitidine 300 mg. The physician did not indicate DAW on the prescription, but the customer insists on getting the brand-name drug. The insurance company will charge him the price of the co-pay, plus the difference in price between the generic and the brand. This is known as *difference pricing*. Calculate the cost to the customer if the generic price is $11.25 and the brand price is $27.95. His usual co-pay is $10.

   Hint: co-pay + (brand price − generic price) = cost

3. A customer wants to pay difference pricing for a prescription for nabumetone 500 mg. The price of the brand-name drug is $85.49 and the price of the generic drug is $17.99. Her usual co-pay is $15. What will the insurance company charge the customer using difference pricing?

4. A pharmacy sets its retail prices as a 30% markup of cost. If a 100-count bottle of acetaminophen 325 mg costs the pharmacy $1.49, what will the retail price be for this item?

PTCB EXAM PRACTICE QUESTIONS

1. What is a drug called that binds to a receptor but does not produce a response?
   a. agonist
   b. antagonist
   c. hormone
   d. neurotransmitter

2. Which organ is responsible for drug metabolism?
   a. kidney
   b. intestines
   c. lungs
   d. liver

3. All of the following drugs may be used to assist patients with smoking cessation *except*:
   a. nicotine patch.
   b. Chantix®.
   c. Dilantin®.
   d. Wellbutrin®.

4. Which organ is responsible for the majority of drug excretion?
   a. kidney
   b. intestines
   c. lungs
   d. liver

5. Drug tolerance usually only involves which of the following components?
   a. physiological factors
   b. psychological factors
   c. the immune system
   d. obsessive compulsive behavior

CHAPTER 20
Drug Classifications

After completing Chapter 20 from the textbook, you should be able to:	Related Activity in the Workbook/Lab Manual
1. List and explain a variety of drug classifications.	Review Questions, PTCB Exam Practice Questions Activity 20-1, Lab 20-1
2. Understand the five pregnancy categories and how they affect drug classifications.	Review Questions, PTCB Exam Practice Questions Lab 20-1, Lab 20-2
3. List and describe the five schedules of controlled substances and identify drugs assigned to each schedule.	Review Questions, PTCB Exam Practice Questions Lab 20-1, Lab 20-3

INTRODUCTION

Pharmacology is a complex, diversified, and intriguing science. To be successful as a pharmacy technician, you need to understand the basics of how drugs are classified, what the classifications mean, and what conditions or diseases the drugs in each class treat. Drugs are classified into categories according to their chemical ingredients, the method by which they are used, and by the body organ they affect. They are further designated by separate classes and groups. Two of the most common classifications are therapeutic usefulness, such as analgesics (used to relieve pain), and pharmacological activity, such as diuretics (used to promote the excretion of urine). Two other important classifications of drugs are: pregnancy categories, which are used to determine the potential harm to the fetus if the drug is taken by a pregnant woman; and controlled substances classes, which are used to indicate the potential for abuse or the addictive nature of the drug.

Many drugs are also available over the counter (OTC). It is an important pharmacy technician duty to understand drug classifications and which drug products are available to patients OTC. This will ensure that the patient receives the best possible care, as properly educated and well-informed pharmacy technicians are much more helpful to both patients and pharmacists.

REVIEW QUESTIONS

Match the following.

1. C edema — a. apprehension, uneasiness
2. a anxiety — b. loss of connection to reality
3. e teratogenetic — c. swelling
4. b psychosis — d. lack of energy, despair, guilt
5. d depression — e. birth defect

Match the brand-name drug with its generic name.

6. meperidine h — a. Inderal®
7. clonidine p — b. Flagy®
8. metronidazole B — c. Nizoral®
9. mebendazole L — d. Thorazine®
10. ketoconazole C — e. Norvasc®
11. acyclovir F — f. Zovirax®
12. cefdinir O — g. Lunesta®
13. clarithromycin N — h. Demerol®
14. enalapril I — i. Vasotec®
15. propranolol A — j. Dilantin®
16. amlodipine E — k. Ativan™
17. lorazepam K — l. Vermox®
18. phenytoin J — m. Restoril®
19. chlorpromazine D — n. Biaxin®
20. temazepam M — o. Omnicef®
21. eszopiclone G — p. Catapres®

Choose the best answer.

22. An example of a calcium channel blocker medication is:
    a. felodipine.
    b. gemfibrozil.
    c. labetolol.
    d. hydralazine.

23. Loop diuretics are indicated for:
    a. osteoporosis.
    b. gout.
    c. infection.
    d. edema.

24. Antiemetics are indicated for:
    a. diarrhea.
    b. nausea and vomiting.
    c. constipation.
    d. acid reflux.

25. A hemostatic drug is used to:
   a. increase blood plasma.
   b. stop bleeding.
   c. prevent blood clots.
   d. break down blood clots.

26. An example of a C-III drug is:
   a. codeine with acetaminophen.
   b. fentanyl.
   c. phenobarbital.
   d. THC.

27. The class of drug that has the highest potential for addiction and abuse is:
   a. C-I.
   b. C-II.
   c. C-III.
   d. C-IV.

28. Which is an OTC antipyretic?
   a. Benadryl®
   b. Pepcid®
   c. Dramamine®
   d. Tylenol®

29. Of the following pregnancy categories, which indicates the lowest risk?
   a. A
   b. B
   c. C
   d. D

30. NSAIDs are used to treat:
   a. inflammation and pain.
   b. fever.
   c. none of the above.
   d. both a and b.

PHARMACY CALCULATION PROBLEMS

1. A medication is to be dosed at 10 mg/kg/day in 3 divided doses. The patient weighs 79 kg. How many milligrams will the patient get in each dose?

2. A patient weighing 182 pounds requires 0.25 mg/kg bolus dose of abciximab. Abciximab comes in a concentration of 2 mg/mL. How many mL will the technician need to draw up for the bolus?

3. Ziprasidone for injection yields a 20 mg/mL concentration after reconstitution. How many mL would be required for a 10 mg dose?

4. 40 units of insulin R must be added to a TPN. If the concentration of insulin R is 100 units/mL, how many mL should be added to the TPN?

PTCB EXAM PRACTICE QUESTIONS

1. Diflucan® (fluconazole) belongs to which of the following drug classifications?
   a. aminoglycoside
   b. antiviral
   c. cephalosporin
   d. antifungal

2. Inderal® (propranolol) belongs to which of the following drug classifications?
   a. calcium channel blocker
   b. beta-adrenergic blocker
   c. ACE inhibitor
   d. antihyperlipidemic

3. Paxil® (paroxetine) belongs to which of the following drug classifications?
   a. antidepressant
   b. antipsychotic
   c. anticonvulsant
   d. antiparkinson

4. Plavix® (clopidogrel) belongs to which of the following drug classifications?
   a. anticoagulant
   b. antiemetic
   c. antiplatelet
   d. thrombolytic

5. Prevacid® (lansoprazole) belongs to which of the following drug classifications?
   a. H2 antagonist
   b. laxative
   c. antidiarrheal
   d. proton pump inhibitor (PPI)

ACTIVITY 20-1: Matching the Disease State/Symptom to the Drug Classification

As a pharmacy technician, you need to be familiar with which drug classifications are used to treat specific disease states or symptoms.

Activity:

The following exercise presents a list of symptoms and disease states and a second list of drug classifications. Review the symptoms and diseases in the first list, then choose the best treatment for each from the second list. Write the letter of the drug classification on the line next to the corresponding symptom/disease state.

Symptoms and Disease States	Drug Classifications
1. _____ allergic reaction due to exposure to cats	a. proton pump inhibitors
2. _____ chronic gastric reflux	b. macrolides
3. _____ exercise-induced asthma	c. antihistamines
4. _____ athlete's foot	d. antihyperlipidemics
5. _____ herpes simplex II	e. antifungals
6. _____ strep throat infection	f. antiemetics
7. _____ high blood pressure	g. antivirals
8. _____ nausea	h. muscle relaxants

9. _____ depression
10. _____ back spasms due to recent injury
11. _____ high cholesterol
12. _____ mild sprained ankle
13. _____ seizure disorder
14. _____ schizophrenia
15. _____ edema and hypertension

i. NSAIDs
j. ACE inhibitors
k. anticonvulsants
l. bronchodilators
m. antipsychotics
n. diuretics
o. SSRIs

LAB 20-1: Memorizing the Top 200 Drugs

Objective:

To memorize the names and uses of the 200 most-prescribed ("top 200") drugs.

Pre-Lab Information:

Review Chapter 20, "Drug Classifications," and the top 200 drug list in Appendix A of the textbook.

Explanation:

It is important for you to know the brand and generic names of the most commonly prescribed drugs, as well as their primary uses.

Activity:

Use the following 12 exercises to help you learn the top 200 drugs.

1. Commonly Used Drugs, Part 1
2. Commonly Used Drugs, Part 2
3. Commonly Used Drugs, Part 3
4. Commonly Used Drugs, Part 4
5. Commonly Used Drugs, Part 5
6. Commonly Used Drugs, Part 6
7. Commonly Used Drugs, Part 7
8. Commonly Used Drugs, Part 8
9. Commonly Used Drugs, Part 9
10. Commonly Used Drugs, Part 10
11. Commonly Used Drugs, Part 11
12. Commonly Used Drugs, Part 12

Note: Duplicate drugs in the top 200 list have *not* been included.

Exercise 1: Commonly Used Drugs, Part 1

Select the generic name of the drug and place the corresponding letter next to the brand name.

Brand Name

1. _____ Advil, Motrin®
2. _____ Ambien®
3. _____ Darvocet-N®
4. _____ Glucophage®
5. _____ HydroDIURIL, Microzide®
6. _____ Keflex®
7. _____ Lasix®
8. __i__ Lexapro®
9. _____ Lipitor®
10. _____ Lortab, Vicodin®
11. _____ Maxzide, Dyazide®
12. _____ Nexium®
13. _____ Norvasc®
14. _____ Prelone/Deltasone®
15. _____ Prinivil, Zestril®
16. _____ Proventil, Ventolin®
17. _____ Singulair®
18. _____ Synthroid/Levoxyl®
19. _____ Tenormin®
20. _____ Toprol-XL®
21. _____ Trimox/Amoxil®
22. _____ Xanax®
23. _____ Zithromax®
24. _____ Zocor®
25. _____ Zoloft®

Generic Name

a. albuterol inhaler
b. alprazolam
c. amlodipine
d. amoxicillin
e. atenolol
f. atorvastatin
g. azithromycin
h. cephalexin
i. escitalopram
j. esomeprazole
k. furosemide
l. hydrochlorothiazide
m. hydrocodone w/APAP
n. ibuprofen
o. levothyroxine
p. lisinopril
q. metformin
r. metoprolol ER
s. montelukast
t. prednisone
u. propoxyphene/APAP
v. sertraline
w. simvastatin
x. triamterene/HCTZ
y. zolpidem

Exercise 2: Commonly Used Drugs, Part 2

Select the correct drug use and place the corresponding letter next to the drug name.

Drug Name

1. _____ Advil, Motrin®
2. _____ Ambien®
3. _____ Darvocet-N®
4. _____ Glucophage®
5. _____ HydroDIURIL, Microzide®
6. _____ Keflex®
7. _____ Lasix®
8. __c__ Lexapro®
9. _____ Lipitor®
10. _____ Lortab, Vicodin®
11. _____ Maxzide, Dyazide®
12. _____ Nexium®
13. _____ Norvasc®
14. _____ Prelone/Deltasone®
15. _____ Prinivil, Zestril®
16. _____ Proventil, Ventolin®
17. _____ Singulair®
18. _____ Synthroid/Levoxyl®
19. _____ Tenormin®
20. _____ Toprol-XL®
21. _____ Trimox/Amoxil®
22. _____ Xanax®
23. _____ Zithromax®
24. _____ Zocor®
25. _____ Zoloft®

Drug Use

a. anti-anxiety (benzodiazepine)
b. antibiotic
c. antidepressant
d. antihyperglycemic (diabetes)
e. antihypertensive (blood pressure and heart)
f. gastric acid inhibitor
g. lipid-lowering agent
h. narcotic analgesic
i. non-benzodiazepine hypnotic
j. NSAID (inflammation and pain)
k. respiratory (asthma and COPD)
l. steroid (inflammation)
m. synthetic thyroid hormone
n. diuretic

Exercise 3: Commonly Used Drugs, Part 3

Select the brand name of the drug and place the corresponding letter next to the generic name.

Generic Name	Brand Name
1. _____ acetaminophen-codeine	a. Prevacid
2. _____ alendronate	b. Lopressor
3. _____ amitriptyline	c. Prozac
4. _____ amoxicillin clavulanate	d. Ativan
5. _____ cetirizine	e. Plavix
6. _____ clonazepam	f. Endocet/Roxicet/Percocet
7. _____ clopidogrel	g. Augmentin
8. _____ conjugated estrogen	h. Advair Diskus
9. _____ cyclobenzaprine	i. Fosamax
10. _____ fluoxetine	j. Effexor XR
11. _____ fluticasone	k. Coumadin
12. _____ fluticasone/salmeterol	l. Paxil
13. _____ gabapentin	m. Klonopin
14. _____ lansoprazole	n. Zyrtec
15. _____ levofloxacin	o. Protonix
16. _____ lorazepam	p. K-Dur/Klor-Con
17. _____ metoprolol	q. Tylenol/Codeine No. 3
18. _____ oxycodone/APAP	r. Cotrim, Septra, Bactrim
19. _____ pantoprazole	s. Neurontin
20. _____ paroxetine	t. Premarin
21. _____ potassium chloride	u. Flonase
22. _____ sulfamethoxazole/trimethoprim	v. Desyrel
23. _____ trazodone	w. Flexeril
24. _____ venlafaxine	x. Elavil
25. _____ warfarin	y. Levaquin

Exercise 4: Commonly Used Drugs, Part 4

Select the correct drug use and place the corresponding letter next to the brand name.

Brand Name

1. _____ Prevacid
2. _____ Lopressor
3. _____ Prozac
4. _____ Ativan
5. _____ Plavix
6. _____ Endocet/Roxicet/Percocet
7. _____ Augmentin
8. _____ Advair Diskus
9. _____ Fosamax
10. _____ Effexor XR
11. _____ Coumadin
12. _____ Paxil
13. _____ Klonopin
14. _____ Zyrtec
15. _____ Protonix
16. _____ K-Dur/Klor-Con
17. _____ Tylenol/Codeine No. 3
18. _____ Cotrim, Septra, Bactrim
19. _____ Neurontin
20. _____ Premarin
21. _____ Flonase
22. _____ Desyrel
23. _____ Flexeril
24. _____ Elavil
25. _____ Levaquin

Drug Use

a. anti-anxiety (benzodiazepine)
b. antibiotic
c. antibiotic (sulfa derivative)
d. anticoagulant
e. anticonvulsant (neuropathic pain)
f. antidepressant
g. antihistamine (allergy)
h. antihypertensive (blood pressure and heart)
i. antiplatelet and clot inhibitor
j. gastric acid inhibitor
k. C-II narcotic analgesic
l. narcotic analgesic w/Tylenol
m. osteoporosis
n. potassium replacement
o. respiratory inhaler
p. skeletal muscle relaxant
q. steroid inhaler
r. synthetic estrogen hormone

Exercise 5: Commonly Used Drugs, Part 5

Select the generic name of the drug and place the corresponding letter next to the brand name.

Brand Name	Generic Name
1. _____ Zyloprim	a. valsartan/HCTZ
2. _____ Lotrel	b. diazepam
3. _____ Wellbutrin SR	c. fexofenadine
4. _____ Soma	d. tramadol
5. _____ Celebrex	e. ranitidine HCl
6. _____ Cipro	f. ciprofloxacin
7. _____ Clonidine	g. ezetimibe
8. _____ Valium	h. rosiglitazone
9. _____ Vibramycin	i. bupropion HCl
10. _____ Vasotec	j. naproxen
11. _____ Zetia	k. valsartan
12. _____ Allegra	l. amlodipine/benazepril
13. _____ Diflucan	m. celecoxib
14. _____ Prinzide/Zestoretic	n. methylprednisolone
15. _____ Mevacor	o. allopurinol
16. _____ Medrol	p. clonidine
17. _____ Naprosyn/Aleve	q. enalapril
18. _____ Altace	r. lisinopril/HCTZ
19. _____ Zantac	s. lovastatin
20. _____ Avandia	t. ramipril
21. _____ Viagra	u. carisoprodol
22. _____ Ultram	v. doxycycline
23. _____ Diovan	w. fluconazole
24. _____ Diovan HCT	x. sildenafil

Exercise 6: Commonly Used Drugs, Part 6

Select the correct drug use and place the corresponding letter next to the drug name.

Drug Name

1. _____ Zyloprim
2. _____ Lotrel
3. _____ Wellbutrin SR
4. _____ Soma
5. _____ Celebrex
6. _____ Cipro
7. _____ Clonidine
8. _____ Valium
9. _____ Vibramycin
10. _____ Vasotec
11. _____ Zetia
12. _____ Allegra
13. _____ Diflucan
14. _____ Prinzide/Zestoretic
15. _____ Mevacor
16. _____ Medrol
17. _____ Naprosyn/Aleve
18. _____ Altace
19. _____ Zantac
20. _____ Avandia
21. _____ Viagra
22. _____ Ultram
23. _____ Diovan
24. _____ Diovan HCT

Drug Use

a. anti-anxiety (benzodiazepine)
b. antibiotic
c. antidepressant
d. antifungal
e. anti-gout
f. antihistamine (allergy)
g. antihyperglycemic (diabetes)
h. antihypertensive (blood pressure and heart)
i. erectile dysfunction
j. gastric acid inhibitor
k. lipid-lowering agent (cholesterol)
l. non-narcotic analgesic
m. NSAID (inflammation and pain)
n. skeletal muscle relaxant
o. steroid

Exercise 7: Commonly Used Drugs, Part 7

Select the generic name of the drug and place the corresponding letter next to the brand name.

Brand Name	Generic Name
1. _____ Vytorin	a. amphetamine
2. _____ Veetids	b. carvedilol
3. _____ TriCor	c. citalopram
4. _____ Seroquel	d. digoxin
5. _____ Pravachol	e. ezetimibe and simvastatin
6. _____ Phenergan	f. fenofibrate
7. _____ Nasonex	g. folic acid
8. _____ Mobic	h. glipizide ER
9. _____ Lantus	i. glyburide
10. _____ Lanoxin	j. insulin glargine
11. _____ Isordil	k. isosorbide dinitrate
12. _____ Glucotrol XL	l. losartan
13. _____ Folvite	m. meloxicam
14. _____ Flomax	n. methylphenidate XR
15. _____ DiaBeta, Micronase, Glynase	o. mometasone
16. _____ Crestor	p. penicillin VK
17. _____ Cozaar	q. pioglitazone
18. _____ Coreg	r. pravastatin
19. _____ Concerta	s. promethazine
20. _____ Celexa	t. quetiapine
21. _____ Calan	u. risedronate
22. _____ Adderall XR	v. rosuvastatin
23. _____ Actos	w. tamsulosin
24. _____ Actonel	x. verapamil

Exercise 8: Commonly Used Drugs, Part 8

Select the correct drug use and place the corresponding letter next to the drug name.

Drug Name

1. _____ Vytorin
2. _____ Veetids
3. _____ TriCor
4. _____ Seroquel
5. _____ Pravachol
6. _____ Phenergan
7. _____ Nasonex
8. _____ Mobic
9. _____ Lantus
10. _____ Lanoxin
11. _____ Isordil
12. _____ Glucotrol XL
13. _____ Folvite
14. _____ Flomax
15. _____ DiaBeta, Micronase, Glynase
16. _____ Crestor
17. _____ Cozaar
18. _____ Coreg
19. _____ Concerta
20. _____ Celexa
21. _____ Calan
22. _____ Adderall XR
23. _____ Actos
24. _____ Actonel

Drug Use

a. angina/heart
b. antibiotic
c. antidepressant
d. antihistamine/nausea
e. antihyperglycemic (diabetes)
f. antihypertensive (blood pressure and heart)
g. cardiac glycoside (heart)
h. CNS stimulant (ADHD)
i. enlarged prostate (BPH)
j. lipid-lowering agent (cholesterol)
k. nasal anti-inflammatory agent
l. NSAID (inflammation and pain)
m. osteoporosis
n. psychotropic (antipsychotic)
o. vitamin supplement

Exercise 9: Commonly Used Drugs, Part 9

Select the generic name of the drug and place the corresponding letter next to the brand name.

Brand Name	Generic Name
1. _____ Accupril	a. benazepril
2. _____ Aciphex	b. cefdinir
3. _____ Aldactone	c. clindamycin
4. _____ Amaryl	d. digoxin
5. _____ Atarax/Vistaril	e. estradiol
6. _____ Avapro	f. gemfibrozil
7. _____ Cleocin	g. glimepiride
8. _____ Climara/Estraderm	h. hydroxyzine
9. _____ Combivent	i. ipratropium/albuterol inhaler
10. _____ Digitek	j. irbesartan
11. _____ Flagyl	k. latanoprost
12. _____ Glucophage XR	l. losartan/HCTZ
13. _____ Hyzaar	m. metformin ER
14. _____ Kenalog	n. metronidazole
15. _____ Lopid	o. omeprazole
16. _____ Lotensin	p. quinapril
17. _____ Omnicef	q. rabeprazole
18. _____ Prilosec	r. risperidone
19. _____ Restoril	s. spironolactone
20. _____ Risperdal	t. temazepam
21. _____ Topamax	u. topiramate
22. _____ Valtrex	v. triamcinolone
23. _____ Xalatan	w. valacyclovir

Exercise 10: Commonly Used Drugs, Part 10

Select the correct drug use and place the corresponding letter next to the drug name.

Brand Name

1. _____ Accupril
2. _____ Aciphex
3. _____ Aldactone
4. _____ Amaryl
5. _____ Atarax/Vistaril
6. _____ Avapro
7. _____ Cleocin
8. _____ Climara/Estraderm
9. _____ Combivent
10. _____ Digitek
11. _____ Flagyl
12. _____ Glucophage XR
13. _____ Hyzaar
14. _____ Kenalog
15. _____ Lopid
16. _____ Lotensin
17. _____ Omnicef
18. _____ Prilosec
19. _____ Restoril
20. _____ Risperdal
21. _____ Topamax
22. _____ Valtrex
23. _____ Xalatan

Drug Use

a. hypnotic (sleep)
b. gastric acid inhibitor
c. antibiotic
d. respiratory agent
e. psychotropic (antipsychotic)
f. cardiac glycoside (heart)
g. diuretic (blood pressure)
h. antiviral
i. prostaglandin (glaucoma)
j. antihyperglycemic (diabetes)
k. antihypertensive (blood pressure and heart)
l. steroid
m. anticonvulsant
n. lipid-lowering agent (cholesterol)
o. estrogen patch
p. antihistamine

Exercise 11: Commonly Used Drugs, Part 11

Select the generic name of the drug and place the corresponding letter next to the brand name.

Brand Name	Generic Name
1. _____ Allegra-D	a. atomoxetine
2. _____ Antivert	b. bisoprolol/HCTZ
3. _____ Benicar	c. cetirizine syrup
4. _____ Cardizem CD	d. desloratadine
5. _____ Cardura	e. diclofenac
6. _____ Clarinex	f. diltiazem CD
7. _____ Cymbalta	g. doxazosin
8. _____ Detrol LA	h. duloxetine
9. _____ Evista	i. fexofenadine/pseudoephedrine
10. _____ Glucotrol	j. glipizide
11. _____ Glucovance	k. glyburide/metformin
12. _____ Imitrex	l. lamotrigine
13. _____ Lamictal	m. meclizine
14. _____ Macrobid/Macrodantin	n. metoclopramide
15. _____ Minocin	o. minocycline
16. _____ OxyContin	p. mirtazapine
17. _____ Phenergan w/codeine	q. nabumetone
18. _____ Reglan	r. nitrofurantoin
19. _____ Relafen	s. olanzapine
20. _____ Remeron	t. olmesartan
21. _____ Strattera	u. oxycodone
22. _____ Voltaren	v. promethazine w/codeine
23. _____ Ziac	w. raloxifene
24. _____ Zyprexa	x. sumatriptan
25. _____ Zyrtec Syrup	y. tolterodine

Exercise 12: Commonly Used Drugs, Part 12

Select the correct drug use and place the corresponding letter next to the drug name.

Brand Name

1. _____ Allegra-D
2. _____ Antivert
3. _____ Benicar
4. _____ Cardizem CD
5. _____ Cardura
6. _____ Clarinex
7. _____ Cymbalta
8. _____ Detrol LA
9. _____ Evista
10. _____ Glucotrol
11. _____ Glucovance
12. _____ Imitrex
13. _____ Lamictal
14. _____ Macrobid/Macrodantin
15. _____ Minocin
16. _____ OxyContin
17. _____ Phenergan w/codeine
18. _____ Reglan
19. _____ Relafen
20. _____ Remeron
21. _____ Strattera
22. _____ Voltaren
23. _____ Ziac
24. _____ Zyprexa
25. _____ Zyrtec Syrup

Drug Use

a. antibiotic
b. antidepressant
c. antihistamine (allergy)
d. antihistamine (dizziness)
e. antihyperglycemic (diabetes)
f. antihypertensive (blood pressure and heart)
g. antitussive (cough)
h. CNS stimulant (ADHD)
i. gastrointestinal (nausea)
j. NSAID (inflammation and pain)
k. osteoporosis
l. urinary antispasmodic
m. narcotic analgesic
n. antimigraine
o. psychotropic (antipsychotic)
p. anticonvulsant (seizures)

LAB 20-2: Understanding Pregnancy Categories

Objective:

Understand the importance of caution when pregnant women use prescription drugs.

Pre-Lab Information:

- Review the pregnancy categories discussed in Chapter 20 of the textbook.
- Visit the following FDA Web site: http://www.4women.gov/faq/pregmed.htm v

Explanation:

Pregnancy categories are determined on the basis of the potential harm a drug may cause to the fetus. The five pregnancy categories of safety are A, B, C, D, and X, with A being the lowest risk and X being the highest. As a pharmacy technician, it is important for you to understand the concept of risk versus benefit—especially as it applies to drugs taken during pregnancy.

Activity:

Visit the following FDA Web site and use the information there to answer the questions related to drugs used in pregnancy: http://www.4women.gov/faq/pregmed.htm

1. Write the definition of Pregnancy Category A as it applies to *human studies only*.

____

____

____

____

2. Write the definition of Pregnancy Category B as it applies to *human studies only*.

____

____

____

____

3. Write the definition of Pregnancy Category C as it applies to *human studies only*.

____

____

____

____

4. Write the definition of Pregnancy Category D as it applies to *human studies only*.

____

____

____

____

5. Write the definition of Pregnancy Category X as it applies to *human studies only.*

____

____

____

____

6. To which pregnancy category does the drug phenytoin (Dilantin®) belong?

____

____

7. To which pregnancy category does the drug isotretinoin (Accutane®) belong?

____

____

8. To which pregnancy category does the drug fluconazole (Diflucan®) belong?

____

____

9. To which pregnancy category does the drug levothyroxine (Synthroid®) belong?

____

____

10. To which pregnancy category does the drug ondansetron (Zofran®) belong?

____

____

LAB 20-3: Recognizing Controlled Drugs

Objective:

To recognize which drugs are in Schedule II and understand how these drugs and prescriptions for them are handled.

Pre-Lab Information:

Review the Controlled Drug Categories in Chapter 20 of the textbook.

Explanation:

Because federal and state laws dictate that Schedule II drugs are maintained and dispensed with greater scrutiny, it is important for you to be able to recognize which drugs fall in this category.

Activity:

Visit the DEA online at: http://www.deadiversion.usdoj.gov/schedules/schedules.htm

Then complete the following exercise designed to help you match brand to generic names for Schedule II controlled drugs.

Controlled Drug Exercise:

Select the generic name of the drug and place the corresponding letter next to the brand name, then list the Schedule (I–V) for that particular drug.

Brand Name	Generic Name	Schedule
1. _____ Ambien	a. zolpidem	_____
2. _____ Ativan	b. triazolam	_____
3. _____ Cocaine	c. thiopental	_____
4. _____ Darvon, Darvocet	d. temazepam	_____
5. _____ Demerol	e. secobarbital	_____
6. _____ Dexedrine	f. propoxyphene	_____
7. _____ Dilaudid	g. phentermine	_____
8. _____ Dolophine	h. pentobarbital	_____
9. _____ Duragesic	i. oxycodone	_____
10. _____ Fastin	j. oxazepam	_____
11. _____ Halcion	k. morphine	_____
12. _____ Klonopin	l. midazolam	_____
13. _____ Librium	m. methylphenidate	_____
14. _____ Lorcet, Lortab, Vicodin	n. methadone	_____
15. _____ MS Contin, Oramorph	o. meperidine	_____
16. _____ Nembutal	p. lorazepam	_____
17. _____ OxyContin, Percocet	q. hydromorphone	_____
18. _____ Pentothal	r. hydrocodone/APAP	_____

19. _____ ProSom
20. _____ Restoril
21. _____ Ritalin, Concerta
22. _____ Seconal
23. _____ Serax
24. _____ Valium
25. _____ Versed
26. _____ Xanax

s. fentanyl _____
t. estazolam _____
u. diazepam _____
v. cocaine _____
w. clonazepam _____
x. chlordiazepoxide _____
y. amphetamine _____
z. alprazolam _____

CHAPTER 21
The Skin

After completing Chapter 21 from the textbook, you should be able to:	Related Activity in the Workbook/Lab Manual
1. List, identify, and diagram the basic anatomical structure of the skin.	Review Questions, PTCB Exam Practice Questions
2. Explain the function or physiology of the skin.	Review Questions, PTCB Exam Practice Questions
3. List and define common diseases affecting the skin.	Review Questions, PTCB Exam Practice Questions

INTRODUCTION

The skin is the largest organ of the body. It consists of three main layers: the epidermis, the dermis, and the subcutaneous layer. Important functions of the skin include serving as a barrier to foreign organisms and debris, managing the regulation of body temperature, excreting salts and excess water, and acting as a "shock absorber" to protect the underlying organs. Unfortunately, the skin plays host to a wide variety of more than 1,000 medical conditions and diseases, ranging from minor irritations to severe infections. Although creams and ointments are widely used to treat skin conditions, treatment options also include oral and injectable medications. As a pharmacy technician, it is important for you to understand the basic anatomy and physiology of the skin and the conditions that affect it, so that you have greater insight into how the drugs used to treat these conditions work.

REVIEW QUESTIONS

Match the following.

1. _____ acne
2. _____ sebum
3. _____ carcinoma
4. _____ pathogenic
5. _____ rosacea
6. _____ mitigation
7. _____ eczema
8. _____ bacteriostatic
9. _____ infection
10. _____ pigmentation
11. _____ bactericidal
12. _____ psoriasis
13. _____ rash
14. _____ parasite

a. oily substance produced by glands
b. an organism living in or on another organism
c. condition of red, inflamed skin
d. disease-causing
e. kills microorganisms
f. inhibits growth of microorganisms
g. inflammatory condition with itch, redness, blisters, and oozing
h. infection plus sebum overproduction
i. invasion of pathogens
j. malignant tumor
k. lessening of severity
l. chronic facial skin disorder accompanied by chronic redness and inflammation
m. coloring of skin
n. noncontagious chronic disease characterized by thick, red, scaly skin

True or False?

15. The skin is the largest organ of the body.
    T F

16. The outermost layer of the skin is the dermis.
    T F

17. Eczema is a chronic immune disorder.
    T F

18. Ringworm is an example of a bacterial infection.
    T F

Choose the best answer.

19. Normal body temperature regulated by the skin is:
    a. 98.6 degrees Fahrenheit.
    b. 89.6 degrees Fahrenheit.
    c. 69.8 degrees Celsius.
    d. 98.6 degrees Celsius.

20. Skin infections are not caused by which of the following?
    a. bacteria
    b. cancer
    c. fungi
    d. viruses

21. The most severe burn would be classified as:
    a. first degree.
    b. second degree.
    c. third degree.
    d. fourth degree.

22. The second most common skin cancer is:
   a. malignant melanoma.
   b. actinic keratosis.
   c. basal cell carcinoma.
   d. squamous cell cancer.

Fill in the blanks.

23. An acute, deep infection of the connective tissue is called ______________.

24. Small red bumps and intense itching caused by mites is known as ______________.

Match the following ulcer descriptions with their classifications.

25. _____ Stage I
26. _____ Stage II
27. _____ Stage III
28. _____ Stage IV

a. lesion extending through skin to the bone
b. crater-like lesion extending through tissue
c. reddening of unbroken skin
d. abrasion or blister

PHARMACY CALCULATION PROBLEMS

Calculate the following.

1. A prescription reads: "Clindamycin 2% in aquaphilic ointment; 60 g. Apply to affected body part twice daily." The pharmacy stocks clindamycin 150 mg capsules. How many capsules will be needed to prepare this compound?

2. A physician has requested a compound for lidocaine 3% in 120 mL calamine lotion. How many milligrams of lidocaine powder must be added to the calamine lotion for the compound?

3. A compound is to contain equal parts nystatin cream, clotrimazole 1% cream, and triamcinolone 0.05% cream. How many grams of each product will be required to make 4 ounces?

4. A physician wants to dilute 100 mL of a 10% topical solution to a 4% solution with sterile water. How many mL of sterile water will you need?

PTCB EXAM PRACTICE QUESTIONS

1. Which is the middle layer of the skin?
   a. subcutaneous
   b. epidermis
   c. dermis
   d. adipose

2. What is an acute, deep infection of the skin and connective tissue accompanied by inflammation?
   a. basal cell carcinoma
   b. eczema
   c. psoriasis
   d. cellulitis

3. What disease is caused by bacteria and an overproduction of sebum?
   a. eczema
   b. acne
   c. psoriasis
   d. cellulitis

4. What kind of skin infection is described as a mycosis?
   a. fungal
   b. bacterial
   c. viral
   d. parasitic

CHAPTER 22
Eyes and Ears

After completing Chapter 22 from the textbook, you should be able to:	Related Activity in the Workbook/Lab Manual
1. List, identify, and diagram the basic anatomical structure and parts of the eye and ear.	Review Questions, PTCB Exam Practice Questions
2. Describe the function or physiology of the ears and eyes.	Review Questions, PTCB Exam Practice Questions
3. List and define common diseases affecting the eyes and ears.	Review Questions, PTCB Exam Practice Questions

INTRODUCTION

Seeing and hearing are two of our basic senses. Although both the eyes and the ears are susceptible to a variety of disorders, these maladies can normally be prevented, controlled, or reversed with treatment, except in rare cases. A wide variety of treatment modalities is available to treat eye disorders. However, it is important that ophthalmic products be used safely and properly, because they are sterile. One of your most important responsibilities as a pharmacy technician is to thoroughly understand the basics of safe using of ophthalmic remedies. As a pharmacy technician, it is important for you to understand the basic anatomy and physiology of the eyes and ears and the conditions that affect them, so that you have greater insight into how the drugs used to treat these conditions work.

REVIEW QUESTIONS

Match the following.

1. _____ humor
2. _____ asymptomatic
3. _____ blepharitis
4. _____ hordeolum
5. _____ cataract
6. _____ cycloplegic
7. _____ conjunctivitis
8. _____ tinnitus
9. _____ glaucoma
10. __a__ photoreceptors
11. __o__ iridotomy
12. _____ retinopathy
13. _____ mucopurulent
14. _____ otitis media
15. _____ mydriatic
16. _____ ophthalmic
17. _____ eustachian tube

a. rods and cones
b. group of eye diseases
c. a noninflammatory disease of the retina
d. pertaining to the eye
e. a drug that causes paralysis of the eye
f. mucus or pus
g. chronic inflammation of the eye
h. showing no evidence of disease or abnormal condition
i. drug that dilates the eye
j. an obscurity of the lens
k. body fluid
l. inflammation of the eyelid
m. infection/inflammation of the middle ear
n. ringing or buzzing in the ear
o. an incision into the iris
p. an infection of the sebaceous gland of the eye
q. connects the ear with the throat

Choose the best answer.

18. The ______________ is often referred to as the "film" of the camera.
    a. pupil
    b. cornea
    c. iris
    d. retina

19. The visual pathway for electrical impulses to the brain is the:
    a. cornea.
    b. sclera.
    c. iris.
    d. optic nerve.

20. Another name for stye is:
    a. hordeolum.
    b. humor.
    c. macula.
    d. conjunctiva.

PHARMACY CALCULATION PROBLEMS

1. A 5 mL bottle of olopatadine, 0.1%, is dispensed for allergic conjunctivitis. If the patient uses 1 gtt ou q8 hr, how many days will the bottle last?

2. How many milligrams of pilocarpine are in a 10 mL bottle of pilocarpine 6% ophthalmic gel?

3. Azithromycin 100 mg/5 mL suspension is prescribed for a child's inner-ear infection. If the patient is to receive 100 mg on day 1 and 50 mg on days 2–5, how many mL will the patient need for the entire course?

4. If cephalexin 500 mg is prescribed qid × 10 days, how many grams will the patient receive over the entire course?

PTCB EXAM PRACTICE QUESTIONS

1. What disease of the eye is characterized by increased intraocular pressure?
   a. conjunctivitis
   b. cataract
   c. glaucoma
   d. macular degeneration

2. What is a condition of the eye in which the lens becomes opaque and interferes with clear vision?
   a. conjunctivitis
   b. cataract
   c. glaucoma
   d. macular degeneration

3. What eye ailment is often referred to as "pinkeye?"
   a. conjunctivitis
   b. cataract
   c. glaucoma
   d. macular degeneration

4. What is the medical term that describes ringing in the ears?
   a. otitis media
   b. tympanitis
   c. tinnitus
   d. vertigo

CHAPTER 23
The Gastrointestinal System

After completing Chapter 23 from the textbook, you should be able to:	Related Activity in the Workbook/Lab Manual
1. Identify the basic anatomical and structural parts of the digestive system.	Review Questions
2. Describe the physiology of the digestive system.	Review Questions

INTRODUCTION

The gastrointestinal system manages digestion in the body. Food is broken down, absorbed, or chemically modified into substances that are required by the cells to survive and function properly. Waste products that the body cannot use are eliminated. The gastrointestinal system extends from the mouth to the anus. Its six main parts are the mouth, esophagus, pharynx, stomach, and small and large intestines. Various supportive structures, accessory glands, and accessory organs also help to make up the complete digestive system. The main purpose of the digestive system is to fuel the body by taking in and metabolizing nutrients.

An estimated 70 million Americans suffer from one or more digestive disorders; this accounts for 13 percent of all hospitalizations. As a pharmacy technician, you should be aware of the most common digestive disorders that require pharmacological treatment, including conditions treated with OTC drugs.

REVIEW QUESTIONS

Match the following.

1. __g__ chyme
2. __e__ mastication
3. __c__ protease
4. __a__ lipid
5. __d__ monosaccharide
6. __b__ µg
7. __f__ pepsinogen

a. fat
b. microgram
c. enzyme that begins protein breakdown
d. simplest form of carbohydrate
e. chewing
f. precursor to pepsin
g. liquid that food turns into before entering the small intestines

Choose the best answer.

8. Which of the following refers to LDL?
- a. bad cholesterol
- b. low-density lipoprotein
- (c.) a and b
- d. good cholesterol

9. Kilocalories (kcal) refers to:
- a. bad calories.
- (b.) food energy.
- c. good calories.
- d. a 1,000-calorie meal.

10. Good cholesterol is referred to as:
- a. high-density lipoprotein.
- b. DRI.
- c. HDL.
- (d.) a and c.

11. A good source of unsaturated fat is:
- a. canola oil.
- b. olive oil.
- (c.) both a and b.
- d. none of the above.

Fill in the blanks.

12. A precursor to pepsin is known as __pepsinoger__.
13. The liver produces __bile__, which is stored in the gallbladder.
14. As chyme enters the duodenum, it must be neutralized by bicarbonate; otherwise, a __duodenal__ ulcer will result.
15. __macronutrients__ are nutrients needed by the body in larger quantities.
16. The only vitamin the body produces itself is vitamin __D__.

Match the following.

17. __c__ cecum
18. __a__ tongue
19. __d__ pharynx
20. __b__ ileum

a. accessory organ
b. small intestine
c. large intestine
d. main digestive system

True or False?

21. GERD occurs because the lower esophageal sphincter relaxes when it should contract.

    T F

22. NSAIDs block the effect of the enzyme cyclooxygenase.

    T F

23. Carbohydrates are bad for our health.

    T F

PHARMACY CALCULATION PROBLEMS

1. You need to compound lansoprazole suspension in a concentration of 3 mg/mL. In this suspension, you will need lansoprazole 30 mg capsules and sodium bicarbonate 8.4% solution. If you need to make 480 mL, how many capsules of lansoprazole will you need?

2. Sucralfate comes in a concentration of 1 g/10 mL. If a patient is receiving 10 mL qid, how many milligrams of sucralfate is the patient receiving daily?

3. A 65-year-old woman weighing 156 lb. is to receive a midazolam IVP dosed at 0.02 mg/kg prior to her colonoscopy. If midazolam contains 1 mg/mL, how many mL will the patient receive?

4. A standard pantoprazole drip at a hospital pharmacy contains 80 mg in 250 mL of 0.9% sodium chloride. If the patient is to receive 8 mg/hr, how many mL will be infused over each hour?

CHAPTER 24
The Musculoskeletal System

After completing Chapter 24 from the textbook, you should be able to:	Related Activity in the Workbook/Lab Manual
1. List, identify, and diagram the basic anatomical structure and parts of the muscles and bones.	Review Questions, PTCB Exam Practice Questions
2. Describe the functions of the muscles and bones and their physiology.	Review Questions, PTCB Exam Practice Questions
3. List and define common diseases affecting the muscles and bones.	Review Questions, PTCB Exam Practice Questions

INTRODUCTION

The musculoskeletal system, which consists of bones and skeletal muscles, provides the body with both form and movement. Its four main functions are to provide a framework or shape for the body, protect the internal organs, allow body movement, and provide storage for essential minerals. The musculoskeletal system is affected by numerous disorders, some of which cause only discomfort and pain, and some of which cause complete disability. Osteoporosis, the most prevalent bone disorder in the United States, affects approximately 20 million Americans, and is a major cause of bone fractures. Osteoarthritis, a progressive disease of the joints, affects up to 40 million Americans.

A wide range of pharmaceuticals is used for the treatment of diseases of the musculoskeletal system, although many provide only symptomatic relief. However, as a result of intensive research, new products aimed at the prevention or retardation of disease, particularly osteoporosis and osteoarthritis, may provide hope for the millions of Americans afflicted with these debilitating diseases. As a pharmacy technician, you should be aware of the most common musculoskeletal disorders that require pharmacological treatment, including conditions treated with OTC drugs.

REVIEW QUESTIONS

Match the following.

1. _____ bones	**a.** tissue that gives shape to ears and nose
2. _____ marrow	**b.** where bones are connected
3. _____ cartilage	**c.** contractile tissue
4. _____ hematopoiesis	**d.** segment of striated muscle
5. _____ joints	**e.** bands holding joints together
6. _____ ligaments	**f.** calcified substance that provides shape and support
7. _____ muscle	**g.** a muscle cell
8. _____ myocyte	**h.** attaches muscle to bone
9. _____ sarcomere	**i.** spongy tissue found inside bone
10. _____ synovial fluid	**j.** fills the space between cartilage and bone
11. _____ tendons	**k.** formation and development of blood cells

Choose the best answer.

12. Smooth muscles comprise or line all of the following except:

a. stomach.
b. lungs.
c. neck.
d. intestines.

13. Which of the following is included in injections as an antirheumatic agent?

a. gold
b. silver
c. copper
d. nickel

Match the following.

14. _____ osteoporosis	**a.** autoimmune disease
15. _____ bursitis	**b.** when white blood cells experience DNA damage
16. _____ myalgia	**c.** bone brittleness due to lack of calcium
17. _____ anemia	**d.** breakdown of joint cartilage
18. _____ leukemia	**e.** when bone breaks down more quickly than it rebuilds
19. _____ osteoarthritis	**f.** failure of bone marrow to produce red blood cells
20. _____ rheumatoid arthritis	**g.** inflammation of small fluid pouches
21. _____ gout	**h.** caused by the deposit of uric acid in joints
22. _____ osteomyelitis	**i.** muscle pain
23. _____ Paget's disease	**j.** bacterial infection of the bone

PHARMACY CALCULATION PROBLEMS

Calculate the following.

1. If an employee gets paid $100/day and has to miss an average of 12 work days each year because of fibromyalgia, how much income is the employee losing each year due to illness?

2. Calculate the monthly medical (traditional and nontraditional) expenses for this fibromyalgia patient:

   medical insurance—$150/month

   medications—$89

   chiropractic and acupuncture—$119

   massage therapy—$45

   physician co-payments—$15

3. If an insurance company pays 60% of the retail price for medications, how much is the customer's co-pay if the total retail price is $223?

4. If a customer's co-payment is $57 and is 30% of the retail price, how much is the retail price?

PTCB EXAM PRACTICE QUESTIONS

1. Which of the following diseases is characterized by loss of bone density and makes the bones prone to fracture?
   a. osteoporosis
   b. osteomyelitis
   c. osteosarcoma
   d. osteoarthritis

2. Gout is a disorder involving the deposit of which of the following compounds in the joints and soft tissues, resulting in significant pain?
   a. potassium chloride
   b. hydrochloric acid
   c. uric acid
   d. calcium chloride

3. NSAIDs are a class of drugs used to treat:
   a. infection.
   b. inflammation.
   c. muscle weakness.
   d. bone loss.

4. All of the following are classifications of arthritis *except*:
   a. juvenile.
   b. osteo.
   c. rheumatoid.
   d. myoclonic.

CHAPTER 25
The Respiratory System

After completing Chapter 25 from the textbook, you should be able to:	Related Activity in the Workbook/Lab Manual
1. Identify and list the basic anatomical and structural parts of the respiratory tract.	Review Questions, PTCB Exam Practice Questions
2. Describe the function or physiology of the individual parts of the respiratory system and the external exchange of oxygen and waste.	Review Questions, PTCB Exam Practice Questions
3. List and define common diseases affecting the respiratory tract.	Review Questions, PTCB Exam Practice Questions

INTRODUCTION

The respiratory system is responsible for providing all cells of the body with the oxygen necessary to perform their specific functions. It is the system involved in the intake of oxygen through inhalation, and the excretion of carbon monoxide through exhalation. The respiratory system is divided into two parts, the upper and lower respiratory tracts. The upper respiratory tract includes the nasal cavity, paranasal sinuses, pharynx, and larynx. The lower respiratory tract includes the trachea, two lungs, two main bronchi, secondary and tertiary bronchi, bronchioles, alveolar ducts, and alveoli.

The most common disease of the respiratory system is the common cold. Uncomplicated common colds are generally treated with OTC medications, including antihistamines, decongestants, cough suppressants, analgesics, antipyretics, and anti-inflammatories. The aim in treatment is to provide relief of symptoms. Naturally, the respiratory system is also prone to more serious diseases and conditions, such as asthma, which affects more than 15 million people and is responsible for as many as 1.5 million emergency room visits and 500,000 hospitalizations every year. If left uncontrolled, asthma can cause a long-term decline in lung function. Because many respiratory diseases are treated with some form of inhalation therapy, it is important for you, as a pharmacy technician, to be able to assist the pharmacist in educating clients as to the proper, safe use of inhalation products. You should also be aware of the most common respiratory disorders that require pharmacological treatment, including conditions treated with OTC drugs.

REVIEW QUESTIONS

Match the following.

1. _____ allergen
2. _____ allergy
3. _____ cilia
4. _____ COPD
5. _____ epiglottis
6. _____ larynx
7. _____ pharynx
8. _____ rhinitis
9. _____ trachea

a. result of immune system reaction
b. inflammation of the nasal passages
c. tiny hair-like organelles in the nose and bronchial passageways
d. windpipe
e. substance capable of causing a hypersensitivity reaction
f. condition resulting from something continually blocking oxygen external exchange in the lungs
g. the voicebox
h. small, leaf-shaped cartilage attached to the tongue that prevents substances other than air from entering the trachea
i. part of the throat from the back of the nasal cavity to the larynx

Choose the best answer.

10. The primary function of the respiratory system is to:
    a. transport air to and from the lungs.
    b. supply oxygen to the blood.
    c. exchange oxygen for carbon dioxide.
    d. keep the brain alive.

11. Chronic obstructive pulmonary disease (COPD) is:
    a. an umbrella term for emphysema and chronic bronchitis.
    b. a serious respiratory disease that makes it difficult to breathe.
    c. partially blocked bronchi and bronchioles.
    d. all of the above.

12. The exchange of gases between blood and cells is called:
    a. pulmonary ventilation.
    b. internal respiration.
    c. external respiration.
    d. cellular respiration.

13. Which does not belong to the conducting portion of the respiratory system?
    a. alveoli
    b. bronchioles
    c. nose
    d. pharynx

14. The structure that closes off the larynx is called the:
    a. glottis.
    b. Adam's apple.
    c. epiglottis.
    d. vocal cords.

15. The exchange of gases occurs in the:
    a. trachea.
    b. bronchioles.
    c. alveoli.
    d. bronchus.

PHARMACY CALCULATION PROBLEMS

Calculate the following.

1. If an inhaler contains 120 metered doses, how many days will the inhaler last if the patient is using 2 puffs qid prn?

2. A patient is using one levalbuterol 0.63 mg nebule in her home nebulizer tid. If levalbuterol comes in a box of 24 nebules, how many boxes will she need for a 24-day supply?

3. A patient is using an albuterol-ipratropium inhaler. The patient is using 2 puffs qid and prn, max 12 puffs/day. If the inhaler contains 200 metered doses, calculate the days supply.

4. How many theophylline 200 mg tablets will be needed for a 30-day supply if the patient takes 1 po tid?

5. A patient received a salmeterol disc-type inhaler from the outpatient pharmacy; the inhaler contains 28 doses. Calculate the days supply if the patient takes one inhalation twice daily.

PTCB EXAM PRACTICE QUESTIONS

1. During respiration, the body inhales ____________ and exhales ____________.
   a. nitrogen, carbon dioxide
   b. oxygen, nitrogen
   c. oxygen, carbon dioxide
   d. carbon dioxide, oxygen

2. Which lung structure is responsible for the exchange of gasses?
   a. bronchi
   b. trachea
   c. alveoli
   d. bronchiole

3. Which of the following is *not* a respiratory disease?
   a. asthma
   b. macular degeneration
   c. COPD
   d. emphysema

4. The Combat Methamphetamine Epidemic Act of 2005 requires nonprescription products to be sold from behind the pharmacy counter if they contain any of the following products *except*:
   a. dextromethorphan.
   b. ephedrine.
   c. pseudoephedrine.
   d. phenylpropanolamine.

CHAPTER 26

The Cardiovascular, Circulatory, and Lymph Systems

After completing Chapter 26 from the textbook, you should be able to:	Related Activity in the Workbook/Lab Manual
1. List, identify, and diagram the basic anatomical structure and parts of the heart.	Review Questions, PTCB Exam Practice Questions
2. Explain the function of the heart and the circulation of the blood within the body.	Review Questions, PTCB Exam Practice Questions
3. List and define common diseases affecting the heart.	Review Questions, PTCB Exam Practice Questions
4. List the total cholesterol, LDL, HDL, and triglyceride ranges for an average adult and describe the differences between HDL, LDL, and triglycerides.	Review Questions
5. Describe the structure and main functions of the lymphatic system, and explain its relationship to the cardiovascular system.	Review Questions, PTCB Exam Practice Questions

INTRODUCTION

The cardiovascular system, or circulatory system, is responsible for transporting blood to all parts of the body. It includes the heart, arteries, arterioles, veins, venules, and capillaries. The arteries are responsible for carrying oxygen-rich blood to the cells while the veins carry the deoxygenated blood back to the heart and lungs. The lungs and respiratory system work in tandem with the cardiovascular system to sustain life. To accomplish its primary purpose as a pumping mechanism that circulates blood to all parts of the body, the heart relies on a conduction system comprised of nodes and nodal tissues that regulate the various aspects of the heartbeat. In addition, the nervous system plays a vital role in regulating heart rate. The lymphatic system and circulatory system also work closely together as blood and lymph fluid move through the same capillary system. Lymph fluid removes wastes and debris from the body and supports the immune system by filtering out pathogens and draining excess fluid from the body.

The two common diseases affecting the cardiovascular system are congestive heart failure (CHF) and coronary artery disease (CAD). Congestive heart failure occurs when the heart pumps out less blood than it receives, resulting in a weakened and enlarged heart, and in less blood being pumped to feed the other organs. CAD is a condition characterized by insufficient blood flow to the heart. Hypertension, or high blood pressure, and hyperlipidemia, or high blood cholesterol, are two additional conditions that affect the cardiovascular system.

Often, both hypertension and hyperlipidemia go undetected, as these conditions do not cause substantial symptoms. As a pharmacy technician, you should also be aware of the most common cardiovascular disorders that require pharmacological treatment, including conditions treated with OTC drugs.

REVIEW QUESTIONS

Match the following.

1. _____ arterioles
2. _____ atrioventricular valves
3. _____ contractility
4. _____ DOC
5. _____ DVT
6. _____ dyscrasias
7. _____ hematuria
8. _____ hyperlipidemia
9. __b__ interstitial space
10. _____ leukocyte
11. _____ venules
12. _____ plaque
13. __g__ phlebitis
14. _____ pulmonary edema
15. _____ proteinuria
16. _____ semilunar valves
17. _____ thrombus

a. smallest of veins
b. body tissue spaces
c. smallest of arteries
d. high concentrations of lipids
e. large quantities of protein in the urine
f. tricuspid and mitral valves
g. inflammation of a vein
h. drug of choice
i. ability to contract and the degree of contraction
j. deep venous thrombosis
k. white blood cell
l. blood clot
m. abnormal condition of the body, especially a blood imbalance
n. aortic and pulmonary valves
o. blood in the urine
p. condition in which fluid collects in pulmonary vessels
q. fatty deposits high in cholesterol

Choose the best answer.

18. The human body contains _____________ of blood.
a. 4,300 gallons
b. 15.6 liters
c. 5.6 liters
d. none of the above

19. The heart muscle pumps _____________ of blood daily.
a. 4,300 gallons
b. 16.6 liters
c. 5.6 liters
d. none of the above

20. The _____________, a double layer of serous and fibrous tissue, is a fluid-filled sac that surrounds and protects the heart. It also permits free movement of the heart during contraction.
a. endocardium
b. myocardium
c. septum
d. pericardium

21. The heart has how many chambers?
a. two
b. three
c. four
d. six

22. Which of the following would be a healthy blood pressure?
    a. 140 over 90
    b. 120 over 80
    c. 120 over 99
    d. 180 over 129

23. Which of the following is not a risk factor for high blood pressure?
    a. genetics
    b. stress
    c. race
    d. heart size

PHARMACY CALCULATION PROBLEMS

Calculate the following.

1. A patient is to receive lidocaine 2 g/250 mL IV that will run at 2 mg/min. What is the infusion rate in mL/hr?

2. If an amiodarone drip is to run at 33 mL/hr for 6 hours, how many milligrams of drug will be infused in that time if the bottle contains 500 mg/250 mL?

3. A patient weighing 240 lb. is receiving dopamine 5 mcg/kg/min IV. The concentration of the dopamine bag is 400 mg/250 mL. What is the infusion rate in mL/hr?

4. A bivalirudin 1 mg/kg IV bolus is needed for a patient weighing 185 lb. How many milligrams will be administered for the bolus dose?

PTCB EXAM PRACTICE QUESTIONS

1. What is the American Heart Association's recommendation for healthy blood pressure levels?
    a. 80/120
    b. 140/90
    c. 120/80
    d. 90/140

2. In the cardiovascular system, ____________ carries oxygenated blood to the cells and ____________ carries deoxygenated blood back to the heart and lungs.
   a. arteries, veins
   b. veins, arteries
   c. arterioles, veins
   d. capillaries, veins

3. Anticoagulants are used to prevent blood clots from forming. Which of the following drugs is an oral anticoagulant?
   a. heparin
   b. warfarin
   c. Lovenox®
   d. Activase®

CHAPTER 27
The Immune System

After completing Chapter 27 from the textbook, you should be able to:	Related Activity in the Workbook/Lab Manual
1. Explain how the body's nonspecific and specific defense mechanisms work to keep the body safe from disease-causing microorganisms.	Review Questions
2. Understand the basic relationships between the immune system and the various body systems.	Review Questions
3. List and describe the different types of infectious organisms.	Review Questions, PTCB Exam Practice Questions
4. List the five stages of progression of HIV to AIDS.	Review Questions
5. Describe autoimmune disease and identify various types.	Review Questions, PTCB Exam Practice Questions
6. Understand how drug resistance develops and what steps can be taken to stop it.	Review Questions

INTRODUCTION

The immune system protects the body from foreign invaders that would otherwise destroy it, or parts of it, via infection or cancer. The immune system uses numerous kinds of responses to attacks from these foreign invaders, and is amazingly effective most of the time. Its defensive barriers and mechanisms include nonspecific mechanisms, such as the skin, mucus and cilia in the linings of the respiratory and digestive passageways, and the blood clotting process. They also include specific defense mechanisms, such as the white blood cells, thymus gland, lymph nodes, antibodies, and lymphocytes (B-cells and T-cells).

Many different classes of medications affect the immune system. These include drugs for the treatment of HIV/AIDS, tuberculosis, and malaria, as well as for many other conditions and diseases of the immune system. Pharmacotherapeutic treatment of pathogens includes antibacterials, anti-infectives, and antifungals, to name a few. As a pharmacy technician, it is important for you to have a clear understanding of what these drugs are and how they work to protect the body.

In addition to fighting foreign invaders, sometimes the immune system is called upon to help defend against the autoimmune process in cases of autoimmune diseases, like lupus erythematosus or rheumatoid arthritis, in which a person's immune system mistakenly attacks itself. The end result of this defense is often inflammation. These autoimmune diseases are treated both pharmacologically and nonpharmacologically. The pharmacotherapeutic goal of treatment is to reduce inflammation, or to stop or suppress the inflammatory process.

REVIEW QUESTIONS

Match the following.

1. _____ aerobic
2. _____ anaerobic
3. _____ antibodies
4. _____ antigens
5. _____ complement
6. _____ DNA
7. _____ epitopes
8. _____ endocytosis
9. _____ hemopoietic
10. _____ genome
11. _____ lysis
12. _____ macrophage
13. _____ pathogen
14. _____ phagocytes
15. _____ RNA

a. process in which cells take up fluids, particles, and other substances
b. the destruction of cells
c. molecules that trigger an immune response
d. blood-forming
e. nucleic acid that carries genetic information
f. nucleic acid that is needed for the metabolic processes of protein synthesis
g. group of proteins that activate a sequence resulting in the death of a substance
h. white blood cell, found in connective tissue and the bloodstream
i. region on the surface of an antibody that is capable of producing an immune response
j. specialized cells that engulf and ingest other cells
k. a disease-causing organism
l. requires oxygen for life
m. complete hereditary material of an organism
n. does not require oxygen for life
o. proteins that specifically seek and bind to antigens

Choose the best answer.

16. Which of the following is not a defense against infection?
   a. mucus
   b. bone marrow
   c. vertebral column
   d. skin

17. Which of the following is not a deterrent to pathogens?
   a. phagocytes or macrophages
   b. lysozymes
   c. tears
   d. none of the above

18. What causes scabs?
   a. clotting factors
   b. flora
   c. proteins
   d. scabbing gene

19. Which are protozoa that most often consume algae and bacteria?
   a. sporozoans
   b. zooflagellates
   c. cilates
   d. ameboids

20. Which have a specialized opening in the outer edge to capture their prey?
   a. sporozoans
   b. zooflagellates
   c. cilates
   d. ameboids

21. Which are parasites that live inside a host and often cause disease to the host by robbing the host of nutrients?
   a. sporozoans
   b. zooflagellates
   c. cilates
   d. ameboids

22. Which of the following is not a solution to resistance?
   a. Avoid using antibiotics unnecessarily.
   b. Complete each antibacterial regimen; do not have leftover pills.
   c. Use the widest-spectrum antibiotic possible.
   d. Use the common antibiotics first.

True or False?

23. A bacillus, or rod-shaped, bacterium has an approximate measurement of 0.5 to 1 µm in width and from 1 to 4 µm in length.
   T F

24. Spirillium is comma shaped or resembles part of a wave.
   T F

25. About 20% of nosocomial bacterial infections (often acquired in hospitals) are resistant to at least one of the most commonly prescribed antibiotics.
   T F

26. Some organisms are resistant to all FDA-approved antibiotics and can be treated only with experimental and potentially toxic drugs.
   T F

Match the following.

27. _____ Stage 1
28. _____ hormones
29. _____ Stage 2
30. _____ chemotherapy
31. _____ Stage 3
32. _____ radiation
33. _____ Stage 4
34. _____ antibodies
35. _____ Stage 5
36. _____ surgery

a. opportunistic infections to a CD4 cell count or level below 200 per cubic millimeter of blood
b. usually the first line of treatment for solid tumors
c. last and final stage of wasting to death
d. may be used in conjunction with other treatments
e. signs and symptoms of HIV begin to show
f. uses cytotoxic agents to kill cancer cells
g. infected without presentation of signs or symptoms
h. prevent cancer cells from receiving signals necessary for continued growth and division
i. initial transmission and infection with HIV
j. used to target cancer cells, depriving the cancer cells of necessary signals or causing the direct death of the cells

PHARMACY CALCULATION PROBLEMS

Calculate the following.

1. If cefuroxime 750 mg IV is administered to a patient tid × 3 days, how many grams will the patient receive over the entire course?

2. A patient has a prescription for acyclovir 200 mg capsules. If the scrip reads, "Take one capsule five times daily for 10 days," how many milligrams will the patient take during the entire course of treatment?

3. Statistically, if one out of every four women has the herpes virus, how many women might be infected at a university with 7,500 women enrolled?

4. Your pharmacy marks up all herbal medication 40% above cost. If a bottle of echinacea costs the pharmacy $3.25, what is the retail price?

PTCB EXAM PRACTICE QUESTIONS

1. All of the following are types of infectious organisms *except*:
   a. yeasts.
   b. bacteria.
   c. viruses.
   d. lipids.

2. AIDS is the result of infection by which type of infectious organism?
   a. yeast
   b. bacterium
   c. virus
   d. parasite

3. All of the following are considered to be autoimmune diseases *except*:
   a. cystic fibrosis.
   b. Crohn's disease.
   c. lupus.
   d. multiple sclerosis.

4. Which of the following classes of antibiotics is divided into four generations?
   a. penicillins
   b. aminoglycosides
   c. macrolides
   d. cephalosporins

CHAPTER 28
The Renal System

After completing Chapter 28 from the textbook, you should be able to:	Related Activity in the Workbook/Lab Manual
1. List, identify, and diagram the basic parts of the renal system.	Review Questions, PTCB Exam Practice Questions
2. Explain the functions of the nephron, kidney, and bladder.	Review Questions, PTCB Exam Practice Questions
3. List and define common diseases and conditions affecting the renal system.	Review Questions, PTCB Exam Practice Questions
4. Explain how homeostasis of fluid and electrolytes affects the body.	Review Questions, PTCB Exam Practice Questions

INTRODUCTION

The renal system, or urinary system, is a fairly simple system with few components; however, its condition has a grave impact on many parts of the body. Genitourinary tract infections, poor kidney filtration, and water imbalance can indicate or cause diabetes, high blood pressure, or dehydration. The proper functioning of the kidneys is essential to maintain life. The drugs most commonly used to treat diseases of the renal system are anti-infectives and diuretics. The use of strong diuretics that help to remove excess water may also cause a loss of potassium, which may lead to muscle and heart problems. A delicate balance of electrolytes, kidney function, filtration, and waste removal must be maintained at all times during illnesses and while taking medications that affect or treat the urinary tract. As a pharmacy technician, you should be aware of the most common urinary system disorders that require pharmacological treatment, including conditions treated with OTC drugs.

REVIEW QUESTIONS

Match the following.

1. _____ acidosis	**a.** pelvic muscle training exercises
2. _____ bilirubin	**b.** empty the bladder
3. _____ dialysis	**c.** a by-product of fat metabolism
4. _____ Kegel	**d.** comparison of a substance's density to that of water
5. _____ ketone	**e.** medical procedure that removes waste from the blood in cases of renal failure
6. _____ palliative	**f.** produced by the breakdown of bilirubin
7. _____ pH	**g.** produced by the breakdown of hemoglobin
8. _____ specific gravity	**h.** excessive acid in the body fluids
9. _____ urobilinogen	**i.** the measure of acidity or alkalinity of a solution
10. _____ void	**j.** reducing the severity of symptoms

Choose the best answer.

11. The specific gravity of water is:
- a. 1.
- b. 2.
- c. 3.
- d. 4.

12. Microscopic kidney cells are known as:
- a. michrons.
- b. nephrons.
- c. nephews.
- d. microns.

13. Which of the following is not a function of the renal system?
- a. filtration of waste from the blood
- b. removal of urine from the body
- c. maintenance of water balance
- d. maintenance of electric balance

14. Phenazopyridine may cause the urine to be colored:
- a. red.
- b. orange.
- c. green/blue-green.
- d. brown/black.

PHARMACY CALCULATION PROBLEMS

Calculate the following.

1. If a patient needs phenazopyridine 200 mg 1 po tid prn × 4 days, how many tablets should you dispense?

2. A new prescription has been dropped off for oxybutynin po, 10 mg bid. If the pharmacy only carries 5 mg tablets, how many tablets will be needed for a 30-day supply?

3. A woman is to receive a trimethoprim/sulfamethoxazole IV for a complicated urinary tract infection. Her dose is 200 mg based on the trimethoprim content. Trimethoprim (TMP)/sulfamethoxazole (SMZ) IV comes as TMP 80 mg/SMZ 400 mg per 5 mL vial. How many mL should be drawn up for the IV?

4. A patient took one hydrocodone/APAP tablet po qid × 5 days for pain from kidney stones. How many grams of hydrocodone did the patient receive if each tablet contained 5 mg of hydrocodone and 500 mg of acetaminophen?

5. If 30% of women will have a urinary tract infection in their lifetimes, how many women could this affect if there are 154 million women in the United States?

PTCB EXAM PRACTICE QUESTIONS

1. Which of the following is considered the functional unit of the kidney?
   a. prostate
   b. ureter
   c. bladder
   d. nephron

2. What is the medical term for difficult or painful urination?
   a. dysuria
   b. hematuria
   c. pyuria
   d. anuria

3. The renal system is responsible for all of the following functions *except*:
   a. filtration of waste from the blood.
   b. maintenance of electrolyte balance.
   c. oxygen transport.
   d. maintenance of acid-base balance.

CHAPTER 29
The Endocrine System

After completing Chapter 29 from the textbook, you should be able to:	Related Activity in the Workbook/Lab Manual
1. Identify and describe the glands of the endocrine system.	Review Questions, PTCB Exam Practice Questions
2. Describe male and female hormones.	Review Questions, PTCB Exam Practice Questions
3. Identify and describe the major diseases and conditions that affect the endocrine system.	Review Questions, PTCB Exam Practice Questions
4. Compare and contrast diabetes mellitus and diabetes insipidus.	Review Questions
5. Understand the effects of anabolic steroid use.	Review Questions

INTRODUCTION

The endocrine system is a collection of glands that produce hormones, substances that help regulate the body's growth, metabolism, and sexual development and function. The hormones, which are released into the bloodstream and transported to tissues and organs throughout the body, influence every cell in some way. The glands of the endocrine system are ductless. The hormones secreted from the endocrine glands are thus released directly into the bloodstream and travel in the body to specific target organs where they exert their effect.

The driving forces of the endocrine system are the hypothalamus, located in the brainstem, and the pituitary gland, which is attached to the base of the hypothalamus. The hypothalamus directs the pituitary gland, which, in turn, controls the thyroid, parathyroid, pancreas, adrenal glands, and the gonads. A complete review of these glands, their secretions, and their effects on body systems illustrates how important the endocrine system is to the proper functioning of the body. For example, every cell in the body depends on thyroid hormones for regulating metabolism.

Some diseases of the endocrine system, such as diabetes, are very familiar to most people; others, such as Graves' disease or Cushing's syndrome, are less common. As a pharmacy technician, you should be aware of the most common endocrine system disorders that require pharmacological treatment, including conditions treated with OTC drugs.

REVIEW QUESTIONS

Match the following.

1. _____ corticosteroid
2. _____ gonads
3. _____ homeostasis
4. _____ hormone
5. _____ isotonic
6. _____ negative feedback
7. _____ polydipsia
8. _____ polyphagia
9. _____ polyuria
10. _____ priapism

a. chemical substance produced by an organ or gland that travels through the bloodstream to regulate the activity of bodily functions
b. process by which the body returns to homeostasis
c. painful, prolonged erection
d. excessive hunger
e. excessive urination
f. a stable and constant environment
g. steroidal hormones produced in the adrenal cortex
h. testes and ovaries
i. characteristic of a solution that has the same salt concentration as that of the blood
j. ingestion of abnormally large amounts of fluid

Fill in the blanks.

11. _____________ is the study of the chemical communication system that provides the means to control a large number of physiologic processes.
12. The _____________ controls the activity of the pituitary gland.
13. The majority of the thyroid tissue consists of the _____________ cells.
14. Thyroid cells combine iodine and the _____________ to make T3 and T4.
15. _____________ are located on the upper part of each kidney.

PHARMACY CALCULATION PROBLEMS

Calculate the following.

1. If the directions for conjugated estrogen cream read, "Apply 0.5 g PV QD," how long will a 60 g tube last?

2. If a diabetic patient gives himself 20 units of insulin tid with meals, how many vials will the patient need for a 30-day supply? The vial contains 10 mL and has a concentration of 100 units/mL.

3. A patient requires a tapering prescription for methylprednisolone 4 mg tablets for a severe allergic reaction. It normally is stocked in a convenience pack, but that form is currently back-ordered.

The patient agreed that she could take the tablets in a bottle as long as all the directions are included. The directions read:

Day 1: Take 6 tablets (at once or in divided doses)

Day 2: Take 5 tablets (at once or in divided doses)

Day 3: Take 4 tablets (at once or in divided doses)

Day 4: Take 3 tablets (at once or in divided doses)

Day 5: Take 2 tablets (at once or in divided doses)

Day 6: Take 1 tablet

How many tablets should you dispense?

4. A man takes 0.125 mg of levothyroxine daily for hypothyroidism. How many micrograms would this man take over 30 days?

5. You just received a prescription for desiccated thyroid 180 mg tablets. The computer system only lists the product in grains. How many grains are in one tablet?

PTCB EXAM PRACTICE QUESTIONS

1. Which disease is characterized by the body's failure to produce insulin?
   a. type 1 diabetes
   b. type 2 diabetes
   c. gestational diabetes
   d. pre-diabetes

2. Graves' disease involves which endocrine gland?
   a. thyroid
   b. parathyroid
   c. pancreas
   d. pituitary

3. Male sex hormones are also referred to as:
   a. estrogens.
   b. progestins.
   c. insulins.
   d. androgens.

CHAPTER 30
The Reproductive System

After completing Chapter 30 from the textbook, you should be able to:	Related Activity in the Workbook/Lab Manual
1. List, identify, and diagram the basic anatomical structures and parts of the male and female reproductive systems.	Review Questions
2. Describe the functions and physiology of the male and female reproductive systems and the hormones that govern them.	Review Questions
3. List and define common diseases affecting the male and female reproductive systems.	Review Questions

INTRODUCTION

The reproductive system is made up of internal reproductive organs, associated ducts, and external genitalia. Its primary function is the reproductive process. Sex hormones are produced in the gonads: in males, in the testes; and in females, in the ovaries.

Although many diseases can affect the reproductive system, a pharmacy technician will most frequently encounter conditions involving contraception, infertility, sexually transmitted diseases (STDs), and benign prostatic hyperplasia (BPH). As a pharmacy technician, it is important for you to be well informed regarding the different types of contraceptives, as well as their side effects and contraindications, and to be familiar with common conditions and disorders of the reproductive system.

REVIEW QUESTIONS

Match the following. Some answers may be used more than once.

1. _____ contraception
2. _____ endometrium
3. _____ hyperplasia
4. _____ oocyte
5. _____ ovaries
6. _____ ovulation
7. _____ ovum
8. _____ STD
9. _____ STI
10. _____ testes

a. reproduction of cells within an organ
b. female reproductive organs that produce eggs
c. process by which an ovarian follicle ruptures and releases an egg
d. sexually transmitted infection
e. male reproductive organs that produce sperm
f. sexually transmitted disease
g. birth control
h. lining of the uterus
i. egg

Choose the best answer.

11. The most abundant and active of the estrogens is:
    a. estrace.
    b. estropipate.
    c. estrodil.
    d. estradiol.

12. Federal law requires that all drugs containing estrogen:
    a. be dispensed with a patient package insert.
    b. also contain progesterone.
    c. be clearly labeled "do not take if pregnant."
    d. have a dispenser.

13. Which of the following will not interact with chemical contraception?
    a. antibiotics
    b. antipyretics
    c. antifungals
    d. antiepileptics

PHARMACY CALCULATION PROBLEMS

Calculate the following.

1. If 0.3% of 2,000,000 women on medroxyprogesterone injection for contraception were to become pregnant, how many women would that affect?

2. If 8% of 5,000,000 women experience PMDD, how many women would that affect?

3. A man has brought in a prescription for prazosin 5 mg capsules. The prescription indicates that he is to take 10 mg bid. How many capsules would you need to dispense for a 90-day supply?

4. For latent syphilis, the recommended treatment is penicillin g benzathine (long-acting), 7.2 million units, divided into 3 weekly intramuscular injections. How many milligrams will the patient receive per dose?

5. A man is receiving 50 mg of testosterone cypionate IM every 2 weeks for hormone replacement. If the clinic stocks testosterone cypionate 100 mg/mL, how many mL of drug will the patient receive over the course of 8 weeks?

Chapter 31
The Nervous System

After completing Chapter 31 from the textbook, you should be able to:	Related Activity in the Workbook/Lab Manual
1. Explain the functions of the nervous system and its division into the central and peripheral nervous systems.	Review Questions
2. Compare and contrast the sympathetic and parasympathetic nervous systems.	Review Questions
3. Describe the function or physiology of neurons and nerve transmission and the various neurotransmitters.	Review Questions
4. Explain the relationship of the nervous system to the other body systems.	Review Questions
5. Explain the functions of the blood-brain barrier and describe what types of substances will and will not cross it.	Review Questions
6. List and define common diseases affecting the nervous system.	Review Questions

INTRODUCTION

The nervous system is a very complex system that interacts with every other system in the body to ensure homeostasis and regulate the body's responses to internal and external stimuli. The nervous system communicates with all cells in the body through nerve impulses that are conducted from one part of the body to another via the transmission of chemicals called *neurotransmitters*.

The nervous system is divided into two parts, the central nervous system (CNS) and the peripheral nervous system (PNS). The central nervous system includes the brain, the spinal column, and their nerves. The peripheral nervous system is also divided into two parts: the somatic nervous system, which controls voluntary movement of the body through muscles; and the autonomic nervous system, which controls involuntary motor functions and affects such things as heart rate and digestion.

Diseases and conditions affecting the nervous system include anxiety, depression, bipolar disorder, Parkinson's disease, alcohol addiction, and seizures. Pain due to injury or cancer also affects the nervous system. *Neuropharmacology*, or pharmacology related to the nervous system, is one of the most diverse and complicated areas of pharmacology. As a pharmacy technician, you must have a solid understanding of the common diseases affecting the nervous system and the pharmaceutical treatments associated with these diseases.

REVIEW QUESTIONS

Match the following.

1. __e__ adjuvant
2. _____ afferent
3. _____ anxiety
4. _____ anxiolytic
5. _____ CNS
6. _____ cerebrospinal fluid
7. _____ EEG
8. _____ efferent
9. _____ gray matter
10. _____ hypotension
11. _____ PNS
12. _____ narcolepsy
13. _____ white matter

a. condition of frequent periods of deep sleep
b. nervous system excluding the brain and spinal cord
c. component of myelinated nerve tissue in the CNS
d. low blood pressure
e. helping or assisting
f. drug used in the treatment of anxiety
g. part of nervous system/brain and spinal cord
h. uncomfortable state of apprehension, worry, and fear
i. nerves sending impulses away from the CNS
j. fluid surrounding brain and spinal cord
k. component of nervous system made up of nonmyelinated nerve tissue
l. nerve sending an impulse toward the CNS
m. graphic record of the electrical activity of the brain

PHARMACY CALCULATION PROBLEMS

Calculate the following.

1. If chlorpromazine 25 mg/100 mL IV is to run over 30 minutes, what is the infusion rate in mL/hr?

2. A patient is to receive 37.5 mg of risperidone long-acting injection. The pharmacy only has 50 mg/2 mL in stock. How many mL are needed for the dose?

3. You need to fill a prescription for duloxetine 30 mg. The directions read "3 caps po QD." The patient only wants a 14-day supply. How many capsules will you need to fill the prescription?

4. If a patient is receiving 0.25 mg of alprazolam tid, how many micrograms is the patient receiving each day?

CHAPTER 32
Pediatric and Neonatal Patients

After completing Chapter 32 from the textbook, you should be able to:	Related Activity in the Workbook/Lab Manual
1. Discuss the differences between neonatal and pediatric patients.	Review Questions, PTCB Exam Practice Questions
2. Explain how the processes of pharmacokinetics in pediatric patients affect drug dosing.	Review Questions, PTCB Exam Practice Questions Lab 32-1
3. Discuss pediatric drug administration and dosage adjustment considerations.	Review Questions, PTCB Exam Practice Questions Lab 32-1
4. List two common childhood illnesses and diseases in pediatric patients.	Review Questions, PTCB Exam Practice Questions

INTRODUCTION

There are many differences between pediatric patients and adults. Pediatric patients are not just small adults, and you must consider a number of factors other than the obvious one of body weight when administering medication. *Neonates* are newborn babies from birth to 1 month of age, whereas *infants* are between the ages of 1 month to 2 years. Finally, a *child* is considered to be between 2 years and 12 years of age.

There are very significant physiologic differences among pediatric patients, and the pharmacokinetic processes known as absorption, distribution, metabolism, and excretion occur quite differently in children compared to adults because a child's organ systems are not yet fully developed. Providing medication therapy to pediatric patients can present a challenge if these differences are not considered. As a pharmacy technician, you need to understand some of the pharmacological differences among neonatal, infant, and pediatric patients; special medication administration considerations; and some of the common disorders that these special patients encounter.

REVIEW QUESTIONS

Match the following.

1. _____ absorption
2. _____ asthma
3. _____ distribution
4. _____ infants
5. _____ intramuscular
6. _____ excretion
7. _____ lipid-soluble
8. _____ metabolism
9. _____ neonate
10. _____ pH
11. _____ pharmacokinetics
12. _____ water-soluble

a. drugs that pass readily into cell membranes composed of mostly fatty substances, such as the brain
b. chemical alteration of drugs or foreign compounds in the body
c. scale that measures the alkalinity or acidity of a substance
d. study of the processes of absorption, distribution, metabolism, and excretion of drugs
e. from birth to 1 month of age
f. drug is absorbed into the bloodstream, then distributed out to the various organs and tissues
g. entrance of a drug into the bloodstream
h. respiratory disease characterized by wheezing and shortness of breath
i. elimination of a drug from the body, usually through urine, feces, or the respiratory system
j. between the ages of 1 month and 2 years
k. drugs composed mostly of water and can be excreted by the kidneys.
l. within a muscle

True or False?

13. The skin of a neonate is thinner than that of an adult.
T F
14. The neonate's digestive system is less acidic than an adult's.
T F
15. A dose that is appropriate for an infant may not be appropriate for a neonate.
T F
16. The liver and kidneys have the smallest blood supply and receive a lower concentration of a drug than other organs.
T F
17. Children usually have a lower percentage of body water and a higher percentage of body fat than adults.
T F
18. Pediatric patients are at risk of drug accumulation and possible toxicity.
T F

PHARMACY CALCULATION PROBLEMS

Calculate the following.

1. Using Young's Rule, calculate a dose of acetaminophen for a 10-year-old child who weighs 65 lb., when the usual adult dose is 500 mg.

2. Using Clark's Rule, calculate a dose of ibuprofen for a 9-year-old boy who weighs 60 lb. The usual adult dose is 800 mg.

3. A child is prescribed antibiotic otic drops for a double ear infection. The product comes in a 10 mL bottle. The directions state "2 gtts AU qid × 10D." How many bottles will be required for the entire course?

4. A woman's state health plan for her child covers three out of the four prescriptions needed, with a $2.00 co-pay for each prescription. The fourth prescription is nonformulary and has a usual and customary price of $24.99. How much will the customer pay for all four prescriptions?

5. A prescription for sulfamethoxazole/trimethoprim suspension has been presented to the pharmacy. The pediatric patient is to take one teaspoonful by mouth twice daily for seven days. How many milliliters will be needed to last seven days?

PTCB EXAM PRACTICE QUESTIONS

1. Newborn children from birth to one month of age are referred to as:
   a. neonates.
   b. infants.
   c. adolescents.
   d. babies.

2. Drug distribution, metabolism, and excretion are quite different in which of the following populations, compared to adults, because their organ systems are not fully developed?
   a. children and adolescents
   b. elders
   c. infants and adolescents
   d. neonates and infants

3. What is one of the most common chronic childhood conditions, affecting nearly 6 million children under the age of 18 each year in the United States?
   a. strep throat
   b. conjunctivitis
   c. appendicitis
   d. asthma

4. What is a serious condition that can occur if strep infections are not treated properly?
   a. chickenpox
   b. measles
   c. rheumatic fever
   d. whooping cough

LAB 32-1: Pediatric Dosing

Objective:

Practice using Clark's Rule and Young's Rule to determine doses for pediatric patients.

Pre-Lab Information:

- Review Clark's Rule and Young's Rule in Chapter 32 of your textbook.
- Review Chapter 14, "Dosage Calculations," in your textbook.

Explanation:

As a pharmacy technician, you may be asked to calculate or check pediatric doses using Clark's Rule and/or Young's Rule.

Activity:

Use Clark's Rule and/or Young's Rule to answer the following questions.

1. A 2-year-old weighing 40 lb. needs phenytoin. The adult dose is 250 mg tid. Using Clark's Rule, how much phenytoin will this child need for each dose?

2. An infant needs furosemide. She weighs 20 lb. and the adult dose is 40 mg bid. Using Clark's Rule, how much furosemide will this child need for each dose?

3. A 6-year-old needs theophylline. The adult dose is 100 mg tid. Using Young's Rule, what is the correct dose for this child?

4. A 10-year-old needs phenobarbital. The adult dose is 60 mg bid. Using Young's Rule, what is the correct dose for this child?

CHAPTER 33
Geriatric Patients

After completing Chapter 33 from the textbook, you should be able to:	Related Activity in the Workbook/Lab Manual
1. Discuss the physiological changes that occur in geriatric patients.	Review Questions, PTCB Exam Practice Questions
2. List several factors that affect pharmacokinetic processes in geriatric patients.	Review Questions, PTCB Exam Practice Questions Activity 33-1
3. Discuss polypharmacy and noncompliance in geriatric medication therapy.	Review Questions, PTCB Exam Practice Questions Activity 33-1
4. Discuss Medicare Part D and its effects on medication dispensing to the geriatric population.	Review Questions
5. Explain ways in which geriatric medication dispensing will change in the future, and how extended life expectancy will change pharmacy practice.	Review Questions Activity 33-1

INTRODUCTION

The number of geriatric patients is increasing, and will affect pharmacy practice in very significant ways. There are nearly 40 million Americans who are 65 years of age or older. Currently, geriatric prescriptions account for the greatest percentage of medication orders filled. Some experts have reported that 50 percent of all OTC products sold today, and 30 percent of prescription medications, are consumed by the elderly. Other factors, such as physiological changes, polypharmacy, multiple diseases, and noncompliance (a patient's refusal or inability to follow a prescribed drug regimen), also affect geriatric medication therapy. As a pharmacy technician, you need to understand the unique factors involved in caring for geriatric patients.

REVIEW QUESTIONS

Match the following.

1. _____ absorption
2. _____ adverse effects
3. _____ bioavailability
4. _____ distribution
5. _____ excretion
6. _____ geriatric
7. _____ half-life
8. _____ metabolism
9. _____ noncompliance
10. _____ OTC drugs
11. _____ polypharmacy
12. _____ side effects
13. _____ toxicity

a. drug poisoning that can be life-threatening or extremely harmful
b. chemical change of drugs or foreign compounds in the body
c. when a patient does not follow a prescribed drug regimen
d. amount of a drug that is available for absorption
e. amount of time it takes the body to break down and excrete one-half of the drug
f. population over the age of 65
g. elimination of a drug from the body
h. undesirable and potentially harmful drug effects
i. entrance of a drug into the bloodstream
j. drug effect other than the intended one; usually undesirable but not harmful
k. administration of more medications than clinically indicated
l. abbreviation for over-the-counter; drugs that can be purchased without a prescription
m. entrance of a drug from the blood to organs and tissues

Choose the best answer.

14. The number of _____________ patients is increasing and will affect pharmacy practice significantly in several ways.
a. adolescent
b. mental
c. cancer
d. geriatric

15. Because the kidneys, liver, and brain are the organs that require the most blood flow to function properly, the _____________ and _____________ processes slow as people age.
a. metabolism, excretion
b. metabolism, absorption
c. excretion, absorption
d. kidneys, liver

16. Which of the following is a common reason for noncompliance by the elderly?
a. dosing schedule is confusing
b. difficulty understanding or remembering what the drug is
c. inability to afford the drug
d. all of the above
e. none of the above

True or False?

17. Organ size generally increases in the elderly, as do blood flow and cardiac output.

T F

18. The patient must sign up for Medicare within 3 months of becoming eligible (3 months before reaching age 65 or 3 months thereafter).

T F

19. By the year 2050, the elderly population will increase to approximately 72 million.
    T F

20. The elderly are projected to consume as much as 85 percent of all OTC medications by the year 2010.
    T F

PHARMACY CALCULATION PROBLEMS

Calculate the following.

1. A normal adult requires 0.1 mcg/kg/min of remifentanil for continuous IV infusion. However, in geriatric patients the dosage should be reduced by half. How many micrograms will a 192 lb. geriatric patient receive over 10 minutes?

2. If an elderly patient with reduced renal function is to receive a 50% reduction in the usual dose of digoxin 0.25 mg, how many micrograms of digoxin should this patient receive?

3. Zaleplon 10 mg is usually given qhs. If a geriatric patient is prescribed half of this dose, how many milligrams will the patient receive over a 14-day period?

PTCB EXAM PRACTICE QUESTIONS

1. Adults experience a decrease in many physiological functions between the ages of:
   a. 18 to 30 years.
   b. 20 to 40 years.
   c. 30 to 50 years.
   d. 50 to 70 years.

2. Which of the following are physiological changes that occur with aging?
   a. increased renal blood flow
   b. increased hepatic blood flow
   c. increased cardiac output
   d. increased body fat

3. Which of the following drugs can cause elderly patients to become dizzy, unsteady on their feet, and possibly fall if the dosage is not adjusted appropriately?
   a. benzodiazepines
   b. diuretics
   c. acetaminophen
   d. ibuprofen

4. Which of the following drugs requires a lower dose in geriatric patients due to reduced renal blood flow?
   a. aminoglycoside antibiotics
   b. thiazide diuretics
   c. penicillin
   d. aspirin

5. Which of the following is a reason for the greater incidence of adverse drug reactions in elderly individuals?
   a. increased cardiac output
   b. decreased intestinal motility
   c. increased kidney function
   d. decreased drug metabolism in the liver

ACTIVITY 33-1: Geriatric Dosing Exercise

Many types of medications require a reduction in the standard adult dose when used for the geriatric population. As a pharmacy technician, you need to familiarize yourself with some of the common classifications that affect the elderly and which doses must be reduced. You should also become knowledgeable about the physical changes that occur as we age.

As our bodies age, we experience many changes. Decreased metabolism and excretion, slowed digestion, and increased fat stores are among the many physiological changes that occur. These are some of many factors that affect how certain drugs are processed. Drugs often stay in an elder's system for a longer period of time, build up to toxic levels in the body, and produce unwanted adverse effects. Kidney function declines over time, and the kidneys play a major role in excretion. Clinical pharmacists and physicians can predict how well or poorly certain medications are excreted by a patient by measuring the amount of creatine produced and filtered. Two laboratory values that are often measured are serum creatine and creatine clearance. These are obtained through a urine sample. The serum creatine level is used to predict the creatine clearance, which indicates the level of kidney function. These two values are very useful tools, but if a patient has very low body fat and has muscle atrophy, these values will not be accurate. The serum creatine and creatine clearance values are usually used in conjunction with another formula, which takes into account the patient's age, weight, and gender. This formula is called the *Cockroft-Gault Equation.*

Physicians and pharmacists need to use caution when using certain drug classes for the elderly. At normal adult doses, these drugs build up in the system and can cause many adverse affects. Some medications can affect the central nervous system, motor functions, cardiovascular system, and gastrointestinal system. Effects can be mild to severe. The dose of almost any type of medication that causes sedation should be reduced. These types include anesthetics, antihistamines, benzodiazepines, non-benzodiazepine hypnotics, narcotics, antipsychotics, and certain antidepressants. If given at normal adult doses, most sedatives (e.g., alprazolam) or sleep medications (e.g., zolpidem), can build up over time, causing excessive drowsiness, dizziness, and confusion. These side effects can also set the individual up for a bad fall, resulting in a hospital stay to repair a fractured hip. Usually, a simple reduction in dose is adequate to maintain appropriate levels in the geriatric body.

Activity:

The following questions state a normal adult dose for a medication. Using the information given, you will calculate the appropriate reduced dosage for a geriatric patient.

1. The normal adult dose of propofol IV required to maintain anesthesia is 12 mg/kg/hr. If a geriatric patient weighs 80 kg, find the infusion rate in mg/hr if you have to reduce the dosage by 50%.

2. If a normal adult dose of diphenhydramine is 50 mg, what is the geriatric dose if it is to be reduced by 50%?

3. A geriatric patient is prescribed trazodone tid. The maximum daily dosage allowed for geriatrics is 75 mg. How many milligrams should be given for each dose?

4. A physician determines that her elderly patient requires a 25% reduction in the normal daily dose of sertraline 100 mg. How many milligrams will be given per dose?

CHAPTER 34
Biopharmaceuticals

After completing Chapter 34 from the textbook, you should be able to:	Related Activity in the Workbook/Lab Manual
1. Name at least two drugs developed by using recombinant DNA technology, and outline their uses.	Review Questions
2. Discuss the four steps in the genetic engineering process.	Review Questions
3. Explain briefly how a company gets approval for a biopharmaceutical drug from the FDA.	Review Questions
4. Discuss why biopharmaceuticals, genetic engineering, and stem cell research are important in the future of pharmacy and the practice of medicine.	Review Questions

INTRODUCTION

Biopharmacology is the branch of pharmacology that studies the use of biologically engineered drugs. *Biopharmaceuticals* are substances created using biotechnology. They can be proteins like antibodies, and even consist of DNA and RNA. Research is being conducted to find new therapeutic medications, or biopharmaceuticals, to treat such life-threatening diseases as AIDS, various cancers, and Parkinson's disease.

Large majorities of biopharmaceuticals are derived from existing life forms, such as plants and animals, although they are produced by means other than direct extraction from a biological source. Genetic engineering is another way to create new drugs; stem cell research also offers opportunities to discover new therapeutic treatments, and is making significant strides in the development of new medications used today. As a pharmacy technician, you should be familiar with some of the concepts of biopharmacology, their impact on the pharmaceutical industry, and their role in the future of pharmacology.

REVIEW QUESTIONS

Match the following.

1. _____ allergenic
2. _____ biologics
3. _____ biopharmaceuticals
4. _____ biopharmacology
5. _____ biotechnology
6. _____ Gaucher's disease
7. _____ GMO
8. _____ MS
9. _____ neutropenia
10. _____ rheumatoid arthritis
11. _____ transformation
12. _____ vector

a. autoimmune disease that causes chronic inflammation of the joints
b. organism that does not itself cause disease, but spreads disease by distributing pathogens from one host to another
c. alteration of an organism itself or the cell in the genetic engineering process
d. disease in which there are an abnormal number of the white blood cells that are responsible for fighting infections
e. substances created using biotechnology
f. substance that can cause an allergic reaction
g. use of biological substances or microorganisms to perform specific functions, such as the production of drugs, hormones, or food products
h. branch of pharmacology that studies the use of biologically engineered drugs
i. organism whose genetic material has been altered using the genetic engineering techniques known as recombinant DNA technology
j. disease in which fatty materials collect in the liver, spleen, kidneys, lungs, and brain and causes the person to be susceptible to infections
k. chronic, inflammatory disease of the white-matter areas of the brain and spinal cord in the central nervous system
l. medicinal products such as vaccines, blood products, allergenics, and proteins

True or False?

13. Biopharmaceutical drugs are used for therapeutic or diagnostic purposes and are defined as pharmaceuticals derived from life forms.

    T F

14. It takes approximately 15 years for a drug to move from the experimental stage to the pharmacy.

    T F

15. During the first, preclinical phase, the company files an Investigational New Drug Application with the FDA.

    T F

PHARMACY CALCULATION PROBLEMS

Calculate the following.

1. A patient who has RA has been prescribed infliximab 2.5 mg/kg for her first dose. Calculate the number of milligrams the patient will receive if she weighs 140 lb.

2. Etanercept is usually dosed at 50 mg SC twice a week for 3 months for severe plaque psoriasis. How many grams will a psoriasis patient receive over 3 months?

3. Find the dose of abatacept needed if a patient weighs 195 lb. According to the manufacturer's recommendation, a patient weighing less than 60 kg should receive a 500 mg dose. If a patient weighs between 60 and 100 kg, the patient should receive a 750 mg dose. If the patient weighs more than 100 kg, the patient should receive a 1,000 mg dose.

4. A patient is to receive rituximab 700 mg IV in 250 mL 0.9% sodium chloride. If the IV is to be infused at 100 mg/hr, how long will it take for the IV to be completely infused?